THE WISDOM OF UNCLE KASIMIR

THE WISDOM OF
UNCLE KASIMIR

GABI CZERNIAK
and
WILLIAM CZERNIAK-JONES

BLOOMSBURY

First published in Great Britain 2006

Copyright © 2006 by Tom and Scarlett Boncza-Tomaszewski

The moral right of the authors has been asserted

Bloomsbury Publishing Plc, 36 Soho Square, London W1D 3QY

A CIP catalogue record of this book
is available from the British Library

ISBN 0 7475 7904 0
9780747579045

10 9 8 7 6 5 4 3 2 1

Typeset by Hewer Text UK Ltd, Edinburgh
Printed in Great Britain by Clays Limited, St Ives plc.

The paper this book is printed on is certified by the © Forest
Stewardship Council 1996 A.C. (FSC). It is ancient-forest friendly. The
printer holds FSC chain of custody SGS-COC-2061

FSC
Mixed Sources
Product group from well-managed
forests and other controlled sources

Cert no. SGS-COC-2061
www.fsc.org
© 1996 Forest Stewardship Council

www.bloomsbury.com

For Tommy

CONTENTS

INTRODUCTION

You can drink from a carafe if you grip its neck and press it to your lips, but if you wish to drink from a spring you must go on your knees and bow your head.

Polish proverb

If you wanted advice in our family, you went to Uncle Kasimir: Polish émigré, self-made millionaire and enigmatic genius (and you always called him Uncle Kasimir, even if, as with both of us, he was actually your great-uncle). Whether or not you went to him looking for advice, you somehow got it anyway. He was the only member of our family who had really seen the world; in the pursuit of war, business and pleasure.

In the Second World War he was a soldier and, later, a spy. After the war, he came to Britain, and by the time he was thirty he had made his first million – precisely how he did so remains a mystery. He filed a number of patents in the late 1940s and early 1950s and it is believed that he 'struck gold' with one of them, but it is hard to find out which one. In 1980 he left this country – some say it was ill-health that drove him out, others that it was the Inland Revenue – and moved to the Swiss Alps with his dog, Anna Karenina III.

As children both of us corresponded with Uncle Kasimir while he was in Switzerland. Our parents encouraged us to write to him, although they were dubious about some of the advice he gave. We treasured our uncle's letters, and often showed our incredulous friends passages in which he told us how to use Napoleonic military strategy to outwit a bully, or explained how to apply Stanisławski's acting techniques to chatting up girls at the pub. He even helped one of us escape from an awful boarding school.

Although our family was quite traditional and mostly of Polish descent, many of our cousins lived a long way away and we didn't see them often. For years we had no idea that Uncle Kasimir corresponded with them, too, over the years providing us, collectively, with an astonishing compendium of advice and wisdom. It was not until 1999, when Uncle Kasimir disappeared and his old camphor-wood chest was sent to us, that we realised the extent of his correspondence: in the chest we found hundreds of letters, photographs, notes, half-completed manuscripts and so on.

We discovered that almost all our cousins had been receiving Uncle Kasimir's advice for a number of years. He was the family's very own agony uncle. As we sorted through the papers we became more and more intrigued. Here we had all the requests for advice, and, often, follow-up letters asking for clarification, or updates on whatever the problem was, but we had none of Uncle Kasimir's letters – none of the actual advice – because he had not kept copies of them. How we yearned to know what they said.

Without much hope of any success, we wrote to all our cousins, aunts and uncles to see if any of them had kept letters from Uncle Kasimir. Amazingly, almost everyone had – even if Kasimir had infuriated or frustrated them. We made photocopies of everything, but were unsure what to do next. Then we had the idea that we could make a book of Uncle Kasimir's wisdom, and in this way share his advice with the world. As we investigated the camphor-wood chest further, we discovered other items of interest, for example Uncle Kasimir's notes on 'Common Mistakes in English', which we think will be of interest to those learning languages, the unpublished manuscripts of a few stories, and a planned, though never broadcast, television drama. Of particular interest were some letters from a woman we had never come across before, named Anastazia Szala. She seems to have been Uncle Kasimir's first love, although we were unable to track her down to find out what he wrote to her.

As we read through the material in the chest we grew to know and love our great-uncle more and more. We believe that a full appreciation of his wisdom comes from a deep knowledge of the man himself, and so we put together a collection of the documents we found most moving, intriguing or educational. The collection we present shows, we hope, our great-uncle's true character, although for reasons of space we have had to leave out a lot of material we would have liked to use.

We should warn you that there is nothing touchy-feely or obviously comforting about Uncle Kasimir's advice or thoughts. Although he could be tender, and even vulnerable, his life has been very hard, and the lessons he has taken from it have not come easily. His was a tough Polish childhood supplemented with 'instructional' beatings from his father ('great military general') and plenty of work. Every Saturday his father made him cut wood with a blunt saw (to build up his strength). Every Sunday, his father would tip out a toolbox full of screws and nails and Kasimir had to sort them (to train his eyes). As a young man, Kasimir was sent from Poland to Russia with two herring sandwiches, in theory to escape the war. After somehow surviving the siege of Leningrad, Kasimir joined the Polish Army and was captured several times before eventually making it to Britain, where he was recruited into the Special Operations Executive (SOE), for whom he carried out several secret missions.

After the war, Kasimir studied chemical engineering and worked as a salesman in his free time, saving money to invest in his own patent applications. By 1950 he was a millionaire. His childhood and his experiences in the war have never left him, however, and he draws on them heavily when giving advice. He has also been involved with the theatre for most of his life. All this has given him material for thousands of intriguing analogies for even commonplace problems of life. Uncle Kasimir is blunt, uncompromising and sometimes even shocking.

He tells the truth, and his advice has always – albeit sometimes in unforeseen ways – worked.

For reasons of authenticity we have not corrected Uncle Kasimir's spelling or grammar, although we were intrigued to note that his English, while often eccentric, was far more accomplished than many of his correspondents'.

When we approached Bloomsbury with the intention of publishing our uncle's letters and documents, we had no idea of the warm support we would receive. In particular we'd like to thank Mary Instone, our editor, for her suggestions regarding the order of the text. We sincerely hope that the general public gets as much out of our uncle's words as we have.

GC and WC-J
Editors

THE PAPER BOY AND THE BULLY

3 February 1988

Dear Uncle Kasimir,

I hope that you are well. How is Anna Karenina III? I hope that she is well too.

You may not remember me because I was very little and had bad asthma when you went to Switzerland. But I hope that you sort of know who I am (your great-nephew William, aged 13) because if it is possible I would like to ask your advice about a problem I am having. Mummy says that you give good advice.

I have got a newspaper round which I do every morning before school. But one of the other boys wants it and he's got his big brother to try and scare me so I won't do it any more and he can. Last week his brother pushed me off my bike at the traffic lights and threw the newspapers into a pond. When I told my boss he said that if I couldn't handle myself he'd have to find someone else anyway.

I really need my job to save up some money. All the children in my class are going to Caen (in Normandy) for a week in the summer term, but Daddy says I have to pay for half of it if I want to go. I know that this boy's brother will get me again soon and then I will get the sack. What do you think I should do?

Yours sincerely,
William Czerniak-Jones

                                        10 February 1988

My Dearest William,

First of all may I say what great pleasure it is to hear from you. You find me in rude health, also Anna Karenina III who is walking on back legs towards my desk for you, out of joy.

Indeed I remember you to be very sickly when I did depart for these shores, but rest assure I do remember you. In any case your mother send me pictures of you at regular intervals, detailing great expense of schooling. You must tell her I am very impress she takes education so seriously.

However, even most rigorous and scholastic environment cannot teach young man all that he is needing to know. Some things can be learn only from experience. This is often best way. My own father, great military general, did once tell me that most important things in life are best learned through bitter experience – for example one time when he shoot several men in his command for theft of chicken and hanging hare. Men were learning hard way not to disobey instruction.

7

Of course when my little nephew is coming to ask me for advice it is a different matter. In these times of peace, with unity of European Common Market, ways of my father are now not necessarily best ways for us all (though some).

You have a predicament which remind me of one occasion when I was myself troubled in similar fashion by Germans – also near Caen, by coincidence, but in 1944. So, you see here there is a symmetry: I will tell you how to solve this problem by following advice gaining in Caen in war, so you can now visit Caen this summer.

Perhaps you will also visit me in Switzerland? As I ask you this Anna Karenina she barks two times – no, also third. It is as if she say to me, 'Kasimir, will you ask this young gentleman to come and visit me in Swiss Alps with spicy Hamburg sausages for me?' Surely you must now come. But what of advice? ('Come to Swiss Alps, come to Swiss Alps,' say Anna Karenina.) I have given this problem my consideration and would ask you to conduct certain investigation for me. All of this must be done within great speed as it is my belief that bully will attack again soon.

First of all, you say this attack happen at traffic lights? Please draw for me sketch of traffic lights including road intersection and surrounding buildings (identify places in which bully might hide) and obstacles such as pond you mention. Secondly, procure for me photograph or sketch of bully in comparison against everyday object so as to indicate size. Then do same for yourself, as photographs your mother has sent me indicate only empty soup bowl on table in front of you.

If you send me this information immediately, situation will be resolve very soon. In meantime, deliver newspapers in different order each day to confuse enemy.

Good luck, and may God be with you in all that you do,

Uncle Kasimir

12 February 1988

Dear Uncle Kasimir,

I hope you are still well. Mummy and Daddy are very glad you have decided to help me, and Mummy says she will think about me going to Switzerland. She also told me to tell you she has just bought me a new school uniform, as she knows how important you think it is for people to look smart.

I have done a drawing like you asked, with everything I could see including a few peacocks that are there and the pond. There is also the big oak tree he was hiding behind. As you may guess it is quite a posh area (although everybody says the garage brings it down), which means that the tips I will get at Christmas should be good!

I drew me and the bully beside a door and an average cat, to give you a good idea of his size. I am not really sure how average the cat is though because we just have one. I think I have also drawn my legs too long which makes me look taller than I am. I really just come up to the bully's arms. He is very big, with a flat head.

I have so far managed to avoid the bully like you said but I know he is after me. I saw him over the road yesterday, watching me. Do you think that is significant?

Your last letter arrived very quickly with no stamp, but in a car from the Swiss Embassy. Mummy says that's the kind of thing you do. I think it's brilliant!

What should I do now?

Yours sincerely,
William

15 February 1988

My Dearest William,

Once again you find me in best of health.

Thank you so much for informative drawing. It tell me all I need to know. Anna Karenina III was surprising for you to choose a cat to indicate size, instead of a dog, but I explain to her that between Pekingese and Wolf-hound there is great difference in size. Between one cat and one other this difference is less pronounce, so you may pat yourself on back for selecting the feline. I believe that cat will be much in same size as any other, reaching at most to middle of bully's shins when cat is sitting in upright position.

Now, you ask me if it is significant bully has been watching you. This is most significant. It prove to me one thing above all other: bully is not pinhead. No doubt he will plan to mount further attack at site of last success, at traffic lights. But bully did not find you at traffic lights when he went to attack you. 'Ha!' he may think. 'By tossing newspapers into pond I have won easy victory and newspaper round is history.' However, his brother tell him later that newspapers were in fact to be delivered on time. Bully think about this and work out newspapers must have been deliver avoiding traffic light intersection. So he watch for you. He move secret around streets each morning searching you out so he may see pattern: one place where you go without failing. One junction you always visit. This is where bully will strike.

During war, as I mention in my first letter, I found myself in very similar situation, only with potential for more serious consequences than loss of newspaper round, for example death by sniper bullet and possible loss of comrades.

After D-Day landing, at Caen I was place in command of small Polish unit with critical mission to take control of mountaintop position from where German forces could be observe. This thing I achieve with ease, but perhaps too much ease. I take motorcycle along winding mountain road to return to commanding officer in Caen. He tell me it will be one week before reinforcement troops reach us, but that reports need to be made to him each day.

'But sir,' I begin.

'Yes?' he reply, eye to me like pike who observe duckling.

'Nothing, sir,' I reply and salute him. He knew already that radio operator is been exploded while we seize control of mountaintop. Luckily man was living, but radio and legs were like spaghetti.

With or without radio, orders need to be obey. And as I ride once again towards unit I did decide that one of my men would need to take same journey on motorcycle each day to make report to military general (inferior, not great military general like my own father).

Mountain road was steep but perfectly sound. Half between Falaise and unit encampment was small village which I was passing through, watch in silence from behind shut window by timid local population. These people live in great terror of Nazis and did not know what to make of dashing Polish officer riding motorcycle through village at speed (similar to Steve McQueen in film *Great Escape*). 'Is this war over?' they ask themself. 'Should we celebrate arrival of Polish forces? What retribution will Nazis deliver if great Allied invasion is failure and we are seen to be supporting enemy?'

But as I drive through village, church bells begin to ring and people begin to fill streets. What is this? I ask myself. I did slow up and park motorcycle at edge of road. Only then I was realising this was of course Sunday and villagers go to attend church service: many of them, old and young. It was most moving sight.

I drove on from village past church, which was locating at crossroads. Pausing to take bearings I feel great pain in arm, followed by crack of rifle shot. This is how it is when you are shot from distance – bullet strike like viper and only then you hear boom of rifle. I throw myself forward on to handle bar and accelerate at speed directly into bushes along side of road, hoping bushes do not conceal brick wall.

Fortune it was favouring me that day because on other side was merely field containing sheeps. Under cover of bushes I throw myself to ground and crawl close to large rock in undergrowth. I inspect arm and discover mere flesh wound. I am lucky man. Peering through leaf I see hill in distance with several trees. Beneath one tree I notice glint of metal – it is sniper.

But sniper is inferior, poorly train marksman. No doubt merely farmer who has experience with shooting ducks. He waste good bullet and betray position. I shout clearly in perfect German: 'Look into air for ducks, simpleton.' Short distance away villagers scuttle into church like little beetle while shots rain down on me, striking soil like hard rain. I stare from below thistle and see now not one but two, then third piece of glinting steel. Three of them, a nest of pinheads.

I pause in stillness of soul, withdrawing revolver from holster, and form plan of action. To escape is no problem as bushes line road in direction of camp – but what of the next day, and day after that? How can I ask my men to do this? To ride through village with shooters on hill? I cannot attack Germans on my own as they are in superior position and have better armament. Even duck-shooter simpleton will no doubt hit target eventually if he fire for long enough. I jump on motorcycle, roar of engine, and escape magnificently, making great show of wheel spinning in dirt and throw many insults. However, when out of sight I stop and beneath drone of overhead bomber I hatch deadly plan to silence nest of pinheads.

I dig deep into memory, struggling to find solution. Feeling ache in arm I wipe blood from jacket and, as I do so, I remember my father's tears as he embrace me on my ninth birthday wearing scarlet tunic smelling of metal.

'My boy, you are nearly man,' he say in low voice, indicating warmth and affection. 'Very soon you will be as tall and strong as your own father.' This I could not believe as I did suffocate in his embrace. 'I have for you present.'

He took me to library and point to lowest shelf. 'My son,' he say, waving hand at row of newly bound leather volumes entitle *Military Strategy*, 'these books will tell you all you need to know.'

I gaze in wonder and begin to count them.

'About what, father?'

'About all things,' he reply, voice like cannon in my ear. 'Within one year you will absorb the knowledge of these books and then I shall examine you.'

'All these books?' I ask, my knees together trembling like reed in swollen river.

'You will read them all. If you are my son, by tenth

birthday you will know this subject inside out, like hide of Bolshevik ripped from bones.'

I counted leather volumes with trepidation, reaching finally twenty-six.

My father he salute me and click heels together, making sound of spine of rabbit snapping in trap. 'And now I will leave you to enjoy birthday,' he say, turning to exit from library. As doors slam shut I did select first volume, full of joy at such generosity. I remember my tears like flooding of River Warta, princess of Polish rivers. Overcome by love for my father, I begin to read.

One year later, on tenth birthday, I stand at my father knee at sunrise and, without making one mistake, answer each one of his questions correctly.

This is why, as I stand beneath droning bomber planes in devastation of Normandy landscape, words of great Frenchman Napoleon sprung at once to my mind:

> When army is inferior in number, inferior in cavalry and in artillery, pitch battle should be avoid. Want of numbers must be supply by rapidity in marching; want of artillery by character of manoeuvres; inferiority in cavalry by choice of positions. In such a situation, it is of great importance that confidence should prevail among soldiers.

My instinct not to launch risky frontal attack on enemy had been correct one. Although inferior to Nazis on several count, my superior intelligence would undo them. In order to defeat them I realise I should make their strength their weakness. My motorcycle it was giving me speed and ability to make intricate manoeuvre and, now I knew precise enemy position on hill, it was I who could take choice of position to attack. My confidence basis on greater Polish morality was of course like concrete brick.

Riding motorcycle across field (again, much like Steve McQueen) I eventually reach other road leading to junction where I was shot at by Germans. From this direction I dismount motorcycle and walk with it until hill with shooters was in evidence. I hide behind broken tree and peer towards hill, only to see German soldiers standing with back towards me, facing village. Fools, I think. Why not also watching road and fields in this direction?

I look behind me and see the reason why. Deep river flowed beyond fields with bridge for road. But bridge was exploded, making impossibility for Allied vehicle and troop to pass. Ahead of me road was also damage: giant bomb crater ripping hole in tarmac, with edges pointing up like old woman fingers towards sky. Pinheads, I think. You anticipate all Allied soldiers to pass through village and wait at crossroads? I laugh and did bestride my motorcycle once more.

With noise of aircraft concealing sound of motorcycle engine I crouch in saddle and rev engine to great speed, thundering like rocket towards bomb crater in road.

Aiming for twisty tarmac, old woman finger, I hit it as ramp to send motorcycle flying like aerial dolphin high above crater, over fence at side of road and into base of hill where bike crash to ground and throw me against bushes.

At this sound, Germans turn quickly, in confusion and disarray. They see smoking motorcycle but not me. I use motorcycle as decoy and crawl through bushes like snake to within inch of German feet. From there I shoot them dead. One is not dead, so I shoot him again.

So you see, in examination of my situation I make strength of potential weakness. Motorcycle make me quick, slippery like eel, but German position of supposing strength make them inflexible and full of confidence. I use my head (not pinhead) to find best position for attack and then, through nerve of steel, my surprise attack it result in victory.

This is what we must do to defeat bully – although not shoot him dead. First you must convince bully that plan to trap you is good one. As I reveal before, he is following you every morning to discover place you always go, where he can be confident to launch successful attack. So far he has not found this or you would be, so to speak, dead man.

Over coming three days you must take different routes on newspaper round, but always leading to traffic lights where first attack take place – as on drawing, beside park near pond. You must time approach so he will see you stop at traffic lights, not just slow down. This will make idiot super-confident.

On fourth day bully will be in for big surprise. From drawing I see large oak tree behind which he was concealing himself last time is only place available for him to hide. As you may have see from adventure I recount above, accurate reconnaissance it is vital and I am assuming your information is accurate.

You will arrive at traffic light junction very early – at least one hour in advance of previous days. With you, you will have all normal things, but also spool of fishing line suitable for landing extremely big fish. Spool must have hole in it so big to fit over handlebars. If there is not one, make with sharp instrument and smooth with file.

Place bag full of newspapers next to oak tree and tie free end of fishing line to it. Loop spool on to handlebars and move bike so is several feet from bag, as if you had throw bag to one side when you stopped. Then get off bicycle and take bicycle pimp, pretending to repair puncture tyre.

Now you wait. Eventually bully he will arrive. He will see you working with bicycle pump and think: Heh, he has puncture. Then he will creep up on you – but not to hurt you. All that bully wants is newspapers to throw in pond again, so little brother can have job. So you must keep eyes open and look in every direction while pretending to work pump. Bully must not realise you see him. Remember: he will think himself clever, stealing up on you to take newspaper bag; and with cover of oak tree it will all be easy for him. He may find this amusing.

Amusing? We shall show him what is amusing.

You are small and nimble; very light so you can move with speed. This I can see from drawing. As soon as bully picks up bag you must jump on to bicycle and begin to pedalling like mad person, encircling bully so that fishing line it bind him to tree. At first he will not realise what is happen as fishing line it is nearly invisible, but after one good circuit you will have him. Once you have gone twice around bully and tree he will be tie fast, unable to fall down, legs pinning to tree: pinleg. But you keep going. Now he will panic, thinking what is happening to him. He will be mad, so angry; but in jaws of trap.

When all of fishing line is use up bully he will be tie to tree and crazy with rage. But rage it will soon becoming fear, and fear becoming humiliation when you place sign at his feet with following words:

HERE STAND BULLY AND THIEF.
HE IS COWARD AND INVITE YOU
TO HEAP HUMILIATION UP ON HIM.
ALL PUNISHMENT IT IS FOR GOOD OF ROTTEN SOUL.

Or similar.

Perhaps you think that bully will come after you like slavering devil when he is at last free. This is unlikely. What will bully say to all of those who have seen him wrap to tree like idiot? What will he tell parents when, perhaps, police are bringing him home and say what has happen? He will not tell them about you, so great will be shame. Spirit will be broken and his life, for the time being, destroy. You will have no more trouble with bully because bully will fear you.

And his brother? Without bully to protect him you can do as you wish with little brother. Bully will possibly give him good beating anyway. Follow my advice to letter, I know you will be successful. You are mouse, bully is lumbering giant. I know which will triumph.

Every bully, every giant, is usually lumbering beast, unable to moving quick. Rooted to spot he will not look in every direction because he is lazy and proud, or so big he cannot do this with effect. As he grow taller he will get further and further away from ground. This make it impossible for him to see what is happening around feet; smaller people they see what is on ground much better and react with superior speed. As ant may be cast into heavens by strong breeze, so small thing is more at risk to forces surrounding it; but like ant, like any small creature, it can detect subtle, almost invisible changes in forces and prepare to engage with them long before giant he realise what is happen. And when small creature negotiate obstacle, sometimes giant may trip up and crash to floor. Big thing is always ripe to fall whereas small thing is in ideal place to grow.

I hope that you will consider my advice with care. Anna Karenina she is eager to know what will become of you. 'Good luck,' she say, 'and do not forget to come to Swiss Alps after Caen.' Now she bark for you. 'Anna!' I say. 'Anna! He will be in touch with us again soon.' So she wag her tail many times.

Remember, have courage like concrete brick and will of steel.

Good luck, and may God be with you in all that you do,

Uncle Kasimir

1 March 1988

Dear Uncle Kasimir,

So I have finally learned who is responsible for my son becoming a delinquent. Naturally he was loath to tell me where he got his ideas from, but I should have guessed. Whatever were you thinking of? Ever since the incident in the park little Christian (the boy William bound so tightly to a tree he stopped breathing and had to be revived on the spot by paramedics) cannot speak without stammering, wakes screaming in the middle of the night and has not spent a full day in school.

William finds it all very amusing, particularly as Christian insists that he had nothing to do with it. Of course that is complete rubbish. Every detail, down to the fishing line William used, is listed in your letters.

And have you forgotten I have to teach at his school? Already there are rumours that my son is a psychopath – many of the children in his class are terrified of him. We study *The Catcher in the Rye* and they do nothing but stare at him.

Well, needless to say he will not be going to Caen this summer; and neither will he be coming to Switzerland to visit you and that ridiculous animal.

In the future if a young boy comes to you looking for advice I suggest you point him in the direction of his parents – or at least think of some more constructive way to support him and his family.

Yours sincerely,
Regina Czerniak-Jones

2 March 1988

Dear Uncle Kasimir,

I am sending this postcard in secret. Don't write back. Mum found your letters. We are in so much trouble. I hope she doesn't get too cross with you. Anyway, it was all worth it, and I wanted to say thanks. I've still got my paper round and I will find some way of talking Mummy and Daddy round so I can come to Europe in the summer.

Lots of love
William

AN ACTOR PREPARES

(undated)

Hi Uncle Kasimir,

Mum asked me to put this in the post for you as she is busy, sorry about the paper it is all I have.

off down the pub now!

Take care.

Urban Winnicki

18 August 1989

Dearest Urban,

Thank you for letter and for a most welcome package of thermal vests. Please also thank your mother for me, and send her – and of course yourself – my very best wishes. Winter will soon be drawing in here in the Swiss Alps and life must go on despite my creaking bones and much snow on ground. These vests will make a big difference to me. Gone are the days when I would clear snow from long winding driveway in a bare chest, and carry logs for my fire on my back, following the instructions from my father

Stanisław, your great-great uncle, who was great (and also possibly great-great) military general in the First World War.

So, you go 'off down pub'. What is this? I try to keep up with the English language, especially so that I can help a dear friend who very much hopes to write a novel in English one day. Is this a public house? Are you a drunkard? Unemployed? Please explain to me.

May God be with you, especially at this time.

Uncle Kasimir

Hi Uncle Kasimir

I am not a drunkard, I am not unemployed, Im currently a student at a college doing a BTEC course in drama. i'm not sure what a public house is, but a 'pub' is where almost all young people go at the weekend, most people go there to relax after a week at work, or college, people also go to meet girls (or boys).

Cheers
Urban

25 August 1989

Dearest Urban,

Although it was I who ask you for advice on simple grammatical matter, I now feel I must offer you some guidance in return. You say you are receiving instruction in the dramatic arts. This is commendable. Yet your letter has no date, and is in poor English. You merely tell me the answer to questions I ask before signing off with your first name and a salutation, 'Cheers', something you no doubt learn in pub. You do not even enquire after my health, or that of my companion, Anna Karenina III.

Do your parents not instruct you in these matters? What about college? It is true that English is a difficult language to learn although for you it must be 'native tongue'. For me, perhaps, it was easier than for some – I learn many language as a boy, under instruction of my most estimable tutor, Blazej Kuss. Of course, before the war education was simple matter for one of my social class. We have no BTEC (what is this?). Also meeting girls (or boys), as you say. This did not happen in a pub. This happen at a dance, or a festival, or by arrangement between parents.

I have one new question for you. I wish to know more about what dramatic arts you learn. Who is your teacher? What he teach you? Do you wish to be Hamlet, or perhaps act in play by Chekhov? Perhaps you do not know I spend much time inside the theatre world after the war, first buying and selling curtain and later as stage-prompt and then actor (amateur only). I have loved theatre since I was a boy.

Perhaps there is something you would also like to ask me? I am, as you probably know, millionaire. I am also expert in life.

Please give warmest regards to your mother, your

father and all of you and yours in that cold and grey but nevertheless nirvana called England, she who I miss, and love as much as my own fragile life.

Your Uncle Kasimir

Dear Uncle Kasimir,

What are you on? honestly and truly there is NOTH-ING wrong with going to the pub sometimes, not in our culture, I only wrote it as something to say, as I do not write many letters and what I wrote looked to short so just dont worry about it, okay. I am NORMAL. Ask mum if you don't believe me, she understands, and I don't know what you think is normal.

I am sorry my letter did not meet your intention but I have been borderline dyslexic since I was 9, a BTEC is a qualification. since you want me to ask you something, how about telling me some good chat-up lines?

Yours sincerely
Urban Winnicki
PS: I hope you and Annie Karenina are alright.

4 September 1989

Dearest Urban

Since you ask, I am on a mountain in Swiss Alps. This I thought that you knew. I am quite well, as is also Anna

Karenina III, who is currently lying on her back dreaming of postman, or perhaps a rabbit, and occasionally saying 'cat' in sleep. Lately she has become obsessed with world of cat. If only our human lives were this simple and fulfil.

Urban, I detect great sadness and in you. Maybe you are, as you say, normal. Perhaps it is normal to be unhappy, to be on borderline of madness (or similar), to lack commitment to studies so you scribble (again in poor English) letters on back of lecture notes and send without stamp. I return notes and have taken opportunity to correct letter on back. You will find this instructional, I am sure.

You ask me if I know any good chat-up lines. This I find interesting. I remember term 'chat up' from after the war, when young ladies would talk of men who would 'chat up' to them, a form of conversation based on flirtation, design to encourage other person to go out with you, or even come to your bed. Perhaps it is because you are drama student that you ask for this advice to be convey in lines. Or perhaps you will write back and again in capital letters tell me this is normal, that we all speak lines in situation of love and even life itself. I will save you trouble by telling you now that we are not marionettes of God. We must speak our own lines and are authors of own lives.

You go to pub because every other person does and you then speak there lines that every person speaks. In London after wartime, amid piles of red and grey debris, in theatre and restaurant, men would say things to young women like, 'Do you come to me often?' and similar phrase, hoping to start conversation. But it was young actors of life who improvise who found happiness, not those following script. Write own lines, Urban, and speak them in every place, not simply in pub.

This is not true in theatre, of course. In theatre, one must speak correct lines and thus provide correct cue for other actors. This I learn when I prepare for my role The Ringmaster in 1957 production *The Unhappy Pony*, existentialist play about machine, automation and free will. In play, there is pony on carousel who does not realise that she is merely machine and wants to instead break free to run in field. My most memorable line, deliver towards end of play was this: 'But know you are made of wood. You cannot run in field. As machine you only work when connected to this bigger machine, this carousel.' Questions asking by play were complex but at same time simple. Are we automata, determined to live out our lives as part of merry-go-round, or are we free thinking beings who must obtain liberty at all costs? Are you man, Urban, or machine?

Next time you want to speak to young companion in pub or even theatre bar or at country dance do not rely on lines that others have created. What do you, Urban, wish to say? Who are you, and how you convey this to young mistress? Your studies they may be poor but you know who you are. You are normal, yes, this you have told me. But in what ways are you not normal? This is what companion will wish to hear. Everyone have unique gift or experience. Talk of these. Improvise around character you know; character of self.

I will now tell you story I think will help.

As youth I was for most part dutiful and obedient. Many long years of training from my father, and also from tutor Kuss, made me into model child. During day I worked hard at my studies, completing sometimes impossible tasks. At weekend I helped father around house and garden. For one hour on a Saturday, I attended Kraków Amateur Dramatics Group, my favourite activity of each week, and a place where I meet with my only friend, Roza. However, on 24 June, in my seventeenth year, I got out of bed a changing man, sullen, uncooperate, disobedient. How this happen? I tell you.

In Poland we have festival, Night of St John, on 23 June every year. In Polish we call this Sobotka, word relating to ritual bonfire. On Sobotka, all young people they would gather on hill or in forest glade to celebrate approaching summer and think of love and fertility. It was important coming-of-age ritual for young man, and for me, especially important as it would be first such ritual I would attend without my father to guide me.

My studies and military preparation had kept me confined in house for most of adolescence, and Kraków Amateur Dramatics Group had only two young member, so I was ill-prepare for how other young people were when together. On Sobotka, I could only stand on sideline as other young men rub stick together for fire (this is part of ritual) and engage in easy conversation, smoke and drink vodka. In another part of glade, young women all dressing in white clothes make garland to throw in river. These garlands are representing virginity, and it was in understanding that on this night only, one couple could become intimate with only promise of marriage, not marriage itself. None of this make impression on me until I did see Roza. Oh yes, she was my friend, but on this night she change. Her hair hung loose down back and white dress flattering small but womanly curve. Oh, my! I long to speak to my friend but suddenly this seem impossible.

As I look at her, one other male he approach me.

'What is name?' he demand.

'Czerniak,' I respond. 'Son of great military general, Stanisław.'

For some reason other boys did laugh at this.

'Who you look at?' biggest male, Alex, ask.

'Roza,' I say. 'She is beautiful like early summer meadow.'

They laugh again. I feel a confusion for first time in life. Why they laugh at my words? What is funny about me, Kazimierz? I did not know. Soon, however, other males stop laughing at things I said, and instead did begin to demonstrate masculinity by jumping over fire, very important part of festival. I was scared of fire and did not want to jump. I manage to stay at back of queue for at least half hour until Alex set dark, no doubt criminal eyes on me and suddenly say, 'Czerniak is not man!'

What is this? I think. How can I not be man? I have read entire library, held sword steady over body of small puppy (by then fully grown Anna Karenina – how I missed her that night), been held upside down over River Warta, princess of Polish rivers, escaped from handcuffs after

Kuss submerge me in same river, face my father on several challenges, including memorable 'duel at dawn', and throw knives at own mother. How could I not be man?

By now some girls watch as Alex and his friends cruelly taunt me. Roza's cheeks were colour of crush rose petals as she lower her eyes to ground. Fire was dying before our eyes like childhood innocence.

'If Czerniak is man,' Alex did continue, 'he will not just jump pathetic dying fire but walk across red hot embers in bare feet. This will prove fertility and show he is truly man.'

They give me three full cups of vodka in preparation for this task.

Eventually, I take off boot and sock and start towards fire, with rough ground beneath feet. I tell myself that I would complete task and prove myself man in front of these mere boys. After all, every task my father and Kuss had given me over years had never been so bad as I imagine. I was not exactly coward, but I was not always so brave either.

At the completion of task I look up to see Roza but she was gone. I turn to other boys, expecting respect now I prove myself man, but they merely laugh at me again.

'Now stand on head,' one of them he say.

I walk in dignified way as possible to edge of river and place burning feet into water and try not to yell out at pain. Suddenly I feel presence of young woman by my side. It is Roza, with servant-girl Anastazia, she help me bathe my feet in silence.

'You are now man,' Rosa say, without looking me in eye. 'It is pity I do not like men.' She then hand me virginity garland and turn to walk away. 'You will never see me again, Kazimierz. I am going to Moscow Art Theatre to study with Konstantin Stanislavski.'

This was like Chekhov play.

It was next morning that I wake up sullen, and with such painful feet. When my father see feet he set off with crossbow and cudgel to find father of Alex. But this did not make me better. I know I was not yet man. In trying to be one other man's idea of man I lose my own true role. I think about Roza, and about what we learn of teachings of Stanislavski, poring over his great works together in hay-loft of her family home. 'It is necessary for actor to immerse himself totally, body, soul and mind, in part he is playing.' Had I not tried to immerse myself in role of man? Yes. But I also remember further teachings of great actor. 'Even if all visible manifestations of character are master, performance it will appear superficial and mechanical without deep sense of conviction and belief.'

This is what I lack, Urban. I, like you, have no conviction or belief in my own role. Again, studying words of great Stanislavski, we learn that actor must always ask three things. 'What? Why? How?' What is pub? Why are you there? How are you to find friend or lover with whom you will not just drink and fall over but share meaning conversation and intellectual pursuit? Good actor will consider all parts of set in which he works and ask, 'What is picture on wall? Why is it there?

How did it get there?' Perhaps picture may show scene of old patriarch rural childhood. Perhaps it is image of dead aunt. Knowing this information will help with character. Perhaps you will also think to ask these questions of yourself. (If you wish to know family history you know you have only to ask me.) Consider also Magic If. When you have problem getting into role – as actor or even role of self, or man – have dialogue with self where each thought it must begin with 'If'. If I were wealthy man . . . If I were great military general . . . If I were in restaurant with girl . . . Be certain about your Ifs and you will becoming more certain about your realities. This also it is truth from Stanislavski.

One last piece of Russian theatrical wisdom remain for me to share with you – concept of purposeful action. This is theory that say you will take action first and feel emotion afterwards. Action it determine character, not other way around. It is no use going to pub all the time and thinking 'But I am interesting person (even with borderline problems).' You will act and <u>then</u> you will be. Go to theatre instead and you will be better drama student and perhaps even better man, although you must decide for self. You will observe that my own act of crossing burning hot coals not make me man. This is because it was not action of man but of confused teenager eager to impress. Consider this and you will learn something.

Please give my fondest regards to your mother and tell her that as winter sets in here I am warm from vests and also from love of family, although distant.

Good luck and may God be with you in all that you do.

Your Uncle Kasimir

3 July 1990

Dear Uncle Kasimir,

Here are the new thermal vests you asked for. How are things in the Alps? We're all busy here, as usual. Urban is off to university in September, to study drama, and little Tommy is not so little any more! (He is currently recovering from a weekend at the Glastonbury Festival.) Adam and I are fine, although just working all the time. Can you believe he still has not been promoted to senior technician? I am still at the law firm, putting in all the hours God sends. Sorry for the short note, I am having a crazy week and it is raining too much even to put washing out. So much for the British summer. The boys, of course, lie on the sofas all the time doing nothing (Urban does occasionally rouse himself to go and practise a play he is in called *Seagulls* – you've probably heard of it). Well, anyway, mustn't complain too much.

Perhaps one day we will all make it to Switzerland for a visit?

Your loving niece,
Lizzie xxx

COMMON MISTAKES IN ENGLISH

14.7.63   English Language
Words and phrases continuing to cause difficulty and embarrassment:–

Haddock/Headache
Important – this point out to me today.

'Good morning doctor I have Haddock.' No. Haddock is fish. This will reveal as foreigner. 'Good morning doctor I have Headache.' This is correct.

(Head – and Hadd – unimportant – to learn is – ache as sounds in cake and – ock as sounds in sock. Kasimir has headache because sun bake. But he buys Haddock from ship in dock. Fisherman can have Headache at sea because he does not catch Haddock. haddock on head, haddock die.)

Experience/Experiment
To say: 'Dinner with you was a memorable Experience, Marjorie.'

Margarine/Marjorie
Marjorie is very kind woman next door. Margarine one does put on toast. Do Not Confuse.

Icicle/Bicycle
Bicycle is what one rides on. Icicle is made of ice. 'I will arrive by icicle' is incorrect.

Kiss/Kuss
English word Kiss sound similar to name of estimable tutor. Do not confuse. Where is he?

Make Use of/Take Advantage of
In hotel I can Make Use of room service maid to tidy room, changing sheets, etc. To Take Advantage of room service maid would be commit despicable act with her.

Bonfire/Bonnet
Bonfire is outdoor fire in field (as in Sobotka). English use to celebrate burning of House of Parliament. Bonnet is hat for girl with ribbon. 'That is nice bonfire on head': Wrong.

Batter/Better
One can Batter haddock (for meal) but Better it with superior meal of steak. A Bettered haddock = steak. Battered haddock = fish. Better meal is superior meal. Good, better, best, <u>not</u> good, batter, bats. To live or to die – which is Batter? No. Neither is Batter. To live is Better.

Gravity/Gravy
Gravity, discover by Englishman Newton and 4th thermodynamic force, very mysterious, is Not same as liquid pour on food at dinner table. 'Please pass Gravy.'

Cellar/Celery
I will go down to Cellar to fetch good wine. Not go down to Celery. Celery is green vegetable for salad. Notice more for 'y' sound at end of words.

Values/Valuables
One cannot leave Values at hotel desk, only Valuables (such as sum of money, expensive watch).

Founder/Flounder
Again, fish. Founder of school is great benefactor. Flounder of school is to be eaten at mealtime. Flounder = also difficulties. 'Is he chairman?' 'No, he is Flounder,' is Not Correct.

Duck/Dick
Duck small bird float on pond. Dick name of man. We go on Sunday to Duck pond, Not Dick pond. People also shout 'Duck' if there is object travelling towards person head. Not Dick.

Kitchen/Kitten
Anna Karenina II likes the Kitten. Not good example. She also likes the Kitchen – favourite room in house. Kitten is small cat. Kit-ten. Speak these words often to learn.

Blackcurrant/Blacksmith
Not again to ask for Blacksmith sorbet.

Butter/Butterfly
Butter like superior margarine. Butterfly is insect with colourful wing. 'Oh, look at pretty Butter.' No.

Exceptionable/Exceptional
He was Exceptional host. Exceptionable host is not good host.

Chopping/Shopping
I am Chopping the wood, not Going Chopping.

Academic/Epidemic
A terrible Academic spread throughout world. An Epidemic is someone who works at university.

Coffee/Coffin
The dead they rest in Coffin. By the side of Coffin you may drink Coffee (like Meursault). Do not offer Marjorie cup of Coffin next time.

Beard/Bear
I was chased in Africa by big Bear, not by big Beard. Beard it is facial hair on man's chin or upper lip, like father.

Bluebell/Bluebottle
Bluebell is pretty flower. Bluebottle is big flying insect, often with blue colouring, as in oil spill. 'My, what an annoying Bluebell' is Not Correct. 'Smell the pretty Bluebells' correct.

Abacus/Abscess
'Dentist, I have Abscess in my mouth,' not Abacus. Abacus for counting. Abscess is bad. Abacus, like Kuss, is good. Kuss have Abacus in classroom, not Abscess.

Blanket/Banquet
He was not given wonderful Blanket to honour him. He was given instead Banquet. In colloquial, person lacking for enthusiasm is not wet Banquet but wet Blanket.

Curry/Carry
'Let me Curry your bags' is not good English. Carry rhyme with marry. I will marry you and then Carry you over threshold.

Terror/Terrier
Marjorie own small highland Terrier.

THE ROBOT FOOT

Editors' note: The following was found in a brown A4 self-addressed envelope in Uncle Kasimir's camphor-wood chest.

6 September 1966

Dear Sirs,

I have enclosed for you perusal the initial chapter of my most recent work, *Adventure of the Robot Foot*.

I was moved to begin writing on advice of my good friend and neighbour Mrs Marjorie Petigrew, former Headmistress, who recommended to me 'Greats' of English literature from her own library. English it is not my first tongue and through works of Dickens, Hardy, Conan Doyle, H. G. Wells, J. Wyndham, and so on, I have achieved far greater and more profound understanding of your language. Like compatriot, great writer Joseph Conrad, I am now in position to write works in this vein, or similar, although better.

Of particular relevance, you may find my interest in scientific matters gain through study at hands of estimable tutor Kuss (although, clearly, certain matter in *Robot Foot* are beyond boundary of his knowledge, for instance computation device, robot machine, space rocket, time travel, foot transplanation, etc) military strategy afford by father, great military general, and matters of the heart.

This tale is set in Victorian London.

I look forwards to hearing from you. Should you wish to take matters further I would be only too pleased to furnish you with remaining chapters of my novel.

Yours sincerely,
Kasimir Czerniak

ADVENTURE OF THE ROBOT FOOT

by Kazimierz Czerniak

In vaults of bank of Bond and Co, London, there is large metal box with well-oiled lid and lock, with name (my own name, for it is mine) painted on it: Herbert J. Wajinski MD. Inside this box you will find, dear reader, many thousands of pages, some hastily scribble in heat of each minute, others carefully written after sound reflection. These pages comprise records of many cases that great detective Rudolph Cape was from one time to another called upon to investigate.

Some, like *Mystery of Little Grange*, where young man went into shed for spade only never to return, or *The Problem of the Erupting Marsh*, where man and little black dog proceed towards moor only to explode, need no further discussion. These cases remain unsolved and serve only to annoy true student of criminal detection. Man and dog may explode, but so may many things: puffball or mountain, and it is naturally so (in both cases through build up of gaseous emission).

Other cases involve private confidence or matters so delicate, often indeed to the State – more than once to the Crown – that they will for ever remain in bank vaults. A select number of cases, however, are suitable for consumption by a general reader. *The Adventure of the Robot Foot*, in which I myself did play a small part in driving ghastly matters to their conclusion is one such tale.

It was icy morning in February and I was hunched over fire grate trying to blow life into embers still glowing from night before. Our housekeeper Birch, formidable woman, had been called to Cornwall because her family was sick two nights previously and, in her absence, Cape had used up entire household supply of matches in completing mathematical puzzle.

'Really, Cape,' said I, cheeks florid from exertions, 'I should start to worry about your good health if you do not cease abruptly.'

Tall, gaunt, his head compressed against walnut table eyeing last of matches, he hushed me.

'Remove three matches from the overall design so that . . . Aha! Wajinski, I have it.' He smile and pick match from the table.

'Well done, Cape. Well done. Now may I have match to light the fire?'

'Wajinski, as ever your lack of enterprise it depresses me.' He reach inside scarlet smoking jacket, withdrew revolver and fired volley of shots into fire grate. Bullets ricochet from the iron, making enormous sparks before shattering one window. My assemblage of twig ignited without further ado and urchin shouted profanity from street:

'Cobblers, sir, cobblers.' As fallen glass tinkle around him.

Cape strode to window. 'Young man,' he shouted. 'I apologise.' And he threw down a half-crown.

'Cor blimey, sir, you are real gentleman.'

Cape turned to me, hint of a smile playing on his cheek. 'Wajinski, as ever, I do you injustice. Your methods may indeed be slow, but what they lack for in speed they gain in security.'

'No, no,' I did say, offering up my hands. 'My dear Cape. It is he who dares, who wins.'

Cape held up his own hand. 'I must stop you at once, Wajinski. Trusted friend. With your method, we would still have window. With mine, fire or no fire we are cursed to suffer chill gust of winter until Mrs Birch is with us once more.'

I gazed at him quizzically. 'Cape, are you not thinking we might resolve the situation sooner? Perhaps if I made call for glazier and –'

Cape raised his hand again, this time with firmness that implied more. 'Wajinsky.' He said no more but met with my eyes. With single twitch of one eyebrow he communicate what outcome to us both of calling glazier behind back of Mrs Birch might be.

Breathing heavily, he strode towards fireplace, picked up chair and smashed it against floor. Gathering pieces of splintered wood he tossed them on to fire before taking pipe from mantelpiece, striking match from table and blowing dark pall of smoke towards ceiling. Like brooding dragon he suck on pipe stem and whistle Slavic folk tune from corner of mouth.

'Tell me, Wajinski,' he said. 'What do you know of electronics?'

'Absolutely nothing at all,' I replied.

'Wajinski, you disappoint me. Boot manufacture?'

'Even less,' I answered glumly.

'Chiropody?'

'Aha,' I said, as I recognise my knowledge of the subject. 'In India my foot cures were infamous. One man could be marching for seven days and I would have him on feet in five minutes.'

'Massage?'

'Good Lord, Cape. How did you know this?'

'That, my good friend, is immaterial. What matters at precise moment is what you are making of this.' He pulled roll of paper from about his person and unfurled it on table.

'Good grief.'

'Quite.'

On one side of the sheet was, quite clearly, impression of big, naked human foot. Of this there was nothing remarkable. Next to it, however, was curious rectangular affair. An oblong block, no less.

'A brick?' I asked, pointing to rectangle.

'Guess again, good friend. If I was to tell you that this wax impression was taken from corpse delivered only yesterday afternoon from mucky waters of Thames, what would you be saying then?'

As was the habit in these situations, I realise that Cape, he tested me. But would I rise to his challenge?

'I say this individual was male,' I began longingly.

'Possibly sizing nine or ten and therefore very probably above average height.'

'Bravo,' yelled Cape, clapping his hands noisily like seal or larger.

'And I say that left foot it was possibly encased in concrete . . .'

Cape shook head vigorously.

'In lead?'

Cape continued with furious shaking, attempting as he was my good friend to drive me towards proper conclusion.

'In some other metal?'

'No.'

'Wood block?'

'What would be the purpose of doing this?' he asked me pointedly, a brilliant interlocutor.

'Why, to drown man, I would imagine.' I raised my hand, palms upwards, expressing this.

Cape he hesitated, took his pipe from his mouth and watched me balefully. 'But if I was to tell you that our man was shot in head, not drowned?'

'Hmmm.' I stared at the image, tracing outline of rectangle with my pinkie finger. 'Then foot and death would appear to be disconnected.'

Cape sighed. 'My lovely Wajinski, many good, wise and respected men would make this same mistake. But once revealed to them that this,' he tapped rectangle shape, 'is *robot* foot, I would suggest they might start think again.'

I gasped deeply, a locomotive moving uphill.

'Yes, *mon ami*,' he slapped my shoulder in conciliatory fashion. 'A robot foot.'

1 November 1966

Dear Mr Czerniak,

Thank you very much for taking the trouble to send us your work.

Your writing does indeed put me in mind of something, but what precisely that is I remain at a loss to say. Many great authors have fashioned works outside their mother tongues, perhaps most notably (as you point out) Conrad; but if I may be so bold, I would suggest you still have a certain distance to go before your work reaches a publishable state.

I hope that you do not find this response too dispiriting. In many ways your writing shows promise. In the future, perhaps you might include a synopsis with your submissions? That is the normal practice.

Yours faithfully,
A. Ball
Literary Agent

IN MEMORY OF DEAD

28 January 1986

On the event of Space Shuttle Challenger Tragedy

Life is very complicated. I have located the problem of death in many divisions as there is so much to say. Perhaps in Poland we have more to say about death than has been said in England, but maybe not so much as in Russia. I shall begin with one incident lodged firmly in mind from my youth.

It is the words of my father, great military general, that I remember in these times: 'You cannot teach anything to dead man.' This he tell me in my ninth year as we drop ashes into the River Warta, princess of Polish rivers. These were ashes of Uncle Felix, impoverished weaver from Łódz who did die by his own hand.

'What would you have wish to teach Uncle Felix?' I say to my father in hushed voice as ashes did swirl among great big lily leaves and trout dead from fuel. My father cuff me three times on cheek with sword hilt (gently so as not to knock teeth) and push my head downwards facing into water.

'What you see?' he ask me loudly, his voice roaring like waterfall over noise of river.

I looked carefully, almost too scared to speak. 'Trout?' I reply, my voice of a whisper. He cuff me again, raising me from earth and shaking me by shoulders. 'Kazimierz, what you see?' This he shout in militaristic voice enough in itself to send Russian scurrying for hole on battlefield.

'The stillness of lily leaves,' I whisper, my teeth chattering from Polish winter and terror of father with arms of steel.

He say nothing but drop me to ground, spitting at that same moment into dark and wintry river waters. In one single movement he grab me by heels and suspend me outright from one arm.

'Kazimierz, what do you see?'

The beckoning darkness of waters beneath head was awful to behold. 'The weeds father, I see weeds.' At this I begin to sob.

'Kazimierz, should one tear from my son enter these same waters containing ashes of my brother, I will no longer have a son. You will float with trout.'

'Yes, father,' I tell him in force voice of nobility. I hold tears from my eyes in my hands and wipe into clothes so not one single drop was spill. I look up to see him watching me, enormous moustache prone and full of dignity above lip.

'Now Kazimierz, I will ask you one more time, what you see?'

My voice was now one of composure, like soldier

about to die for greater glory. 'Father, I see nothing. I see nothing at all.'

'That is my boy,' he say, laughing deeply like jet turbine. 'You see nothing. Uncle Felix he was nothing and now in death he remains nothing. Nothing is rejoin with nothing. "Gigni de nihilo nihilum, in nihilum nil posse reverti." With his own hand he take his life out of fear. Fear of what? What is there to fear unless you have never truly known fear?'

My head at this point it was rushing and dizzy with blood from my suspension upside down so long.

'I who have had cannon ball explode into my face, who watch greater man than he cut down by peasant fool too ignorant to sign own name. I who have felt heat of battle and pain of bullets tearing flesh. How many times I have cut bullets from my own flesh, Kazimierz? Answer me this.'

'Sixteen times, father.' All sixteen bullets I present, naturally, in row at end of bed alongside tin soldiers, but taller and tint of my father blood.

'And blade of my knife is how long?'

'Seven inches, father. It is great blade.'

'Ha. You ask me what I would teach Felix? I would teach Felix nothing. What he could not learn in his own life is not worth knowing.'

So you see, life it is so complicate. If life is live in fear and ignorance, ever looking inwardly, it would as easily not have been live at all. Man such as my father, great military general, did seize upon life as he seize upon my own heels over River Warta. He know no fear, but only because he did know such fear. He did not shrink from death, but only because he face death in excess of sixteen times. By occasion of his retirement – great state event celebrated by dancing Lipizzan horses from Czechoslovakia, processions throughout Warsaw and imposing statue in iron later destroy by Nazi decree – I have many more bullets, at least sixty-four, although several were fire from same automatic weapon into my father's leg.

In England you say, 'A coward die many times, but brave man only once.' My father he say, 'A brave man may die in pain but coward dies always in torment.'

God rest souls of all those who are dead, for they will remain so.

LETTERS FROM NEW YORK

(Editors' note: the following correspondence was found tied together with a black ribbon, right at the bottom of the camphor-wood chest. We have no idea where Anastazia Szala/Anna Small is now, and no record of what Kasimir wrote to her.)

13 August 1947

Kasi,
   You safe. I happy. You say wrote inglisch.
   This all can.

Anastazia
xxx

16 August 1947

Kasi,
   I not can letter. Inglisch bad.
   I am love.

Ana
x

10 September 1947

Kasi,

This picture, it me. I live in flat.

A

x

*(Editors' note: the postcard shows the Statue of
Liberty with a bird perched on the torch.)*

21 October 1947

Kasimir,

Your letter it not read. I go night school learn read.
Mrs Polinsky from beneath has me help with this. She
good inglisch. Why you not let me write Polish?

Your Ana

xx

31 December 1947

Kasi,

New year. Where you? I throw class. Bad.
Mrs Polinsky she still helping Englisch.

Ana xx

*(Editors' note: there are eighteen more postcards
postmarked between 1947 and 1950. However, the
ink has faded and, apart from the stamp and
postmark, no text remains.)*

12 July 1950

Kasimir,

The city, the city. It is suck all life form of me.
This is all for today.

Ana

x

24 July 1950

Kasi,

You has sending Bond Street chocolate also silk scarf.
I in new Night school.

Thank you

Ana xxx

13 December 1950

I wish I understanding your letters. Kasi, come to New
York?

Ana xx

24 December 1950

Kasimir,

Here am me, alone one more time. How you do this? You say not come. Why? In city man he selling brown hot fruit and everywhere is light for Christmas. In shop is Santa Man and on ice lake children they do skate, and they do laugh in group. Alone in city and I feeling alone as on iceberg like Titanic after person all jumping.

I am sink ship.

You me sink.

In sad,
Anastazia

21 January 1951

Kasimir,

You sending list of Englisch word for why? I not understand. I am cleaning office each day as job and flat has rat.

You still not come.

Anastazia

14 February 1951

Kasi,

You send again chocolate. I will eat chocolate but send you money back. I make own fortune in city. If you would send self and not money that it would be better.

Your Ana xx

12 March 1951

Kasimir,

At last I am understand more Englisch. I read old letter from you. I know how you are arriving in Ingland in small boat. I arrive New York in big boat. Many people are turn away. I give name 'Small' and here in big apple I is Anna Small but always I will for you being Ana Szala.

Remember spring in Kraków: thaw of ice, bird they sing, we kiss together.

Kindly regards
Miss Anna Small

24 June 1951

Kasi,

I not have letter from you in two month. You say you are leaving Mrs B house but do not give forward address. Do not leave me alone in this world, I beg of you.

I go English class still and learn not only English but also matter of US constitution, pilgrim forehead, Abe Lincoln, cowboy, gold rush, prohibition, depressing, atom bomb and so forth. I am top of class! Can you believe your Ana, orphan of Kraków, servant girl, and now cleaner in big apple, with only rat for company, she can be top of class?

Do not forget your Ana.

In faithfulness
Miss Anna Small
xxx

13 July 1951

Kasi,

I still not hearing from you. You love perhaps another? Who she?

It hot here, day and night, with people they sleep with door and window open and thing they catch fire and truck they go 'beep beep' down road day and night to rescue people from lick of flame.

I read first book in Englisch, it is wrote by John Stienbeck, *Of Mice and Men*. We study in night school. Teacher he say if I keep top of class I can enrol on new night school learning perhaps tapestry, secretary or grammar.

I never forget you.

Ana xxx

5 August 1951

Kasimir,

You are now living Knightsbridge, London. You finish diploma. This you telling me. You not telling me any matter important. When you come? Do you still thinking of me? Tell truth Kasi. I OK with only rat.

Men they ask me go dance. I say I have other. Is true?

Anna Small (Miss)
Your Ana
Yours truly
xxx

15 September 1951

Kasimir,

What kind of man he sending money, fountain pen, chocolate, caviare fish egg but not self?

I am in new grade at night school. Secretary.

Ana xxx

1 October 1951

Kasimir,
  I hate you.

Anastazia Szala
(once true love, now nothing, zero)

2 October 1951

Kasimir,
  I hate you.

AS

3 October 1951

I hate you.

A. Small

24 December 1951

Dear Kasimir,
  I hope you are in fine health. My heart is still broken.
Christmas is the same in this city of lonely souls.

Children skate on ice unaware of death which come to all. Men they hurry into shop for jewellery for wife, thinking not of rust. I hope you happy in life of choice.

This evening I drink Krupnik alone. Even rat is dead.

Ana Szala
(she who you once love)

12 June 1952

Dear Kasimir,

Why do you still write to me? I enjoy your letters but do you not remember breaking up with me last year? I hope you are happy. I am not.

Yours sincerely,
Anna

13 September 1952

Kasi,

Look how good my English is now. Here I am alone in my apartment, and the end of summer is also the end of this life for me. Kasi, I am secretary now in legal firm and a lawyer, Paul, has asked me to marry him. I have said 'yes', but in my heart I only say yes to you. I want you to know this.

You know where I am, Kasi. I here until wedding in October.

Your Ana

New Jersey
21 October 1952

Dear Mr Czerniak,

Please desist from writing letters to my wife. Whatever was between you is now in the past and you must understand that. I love Anna very much and we are happy in our life together. I am happy for her to correspond with friends and family from Europe. However, when she receives a letter from you she is upset for days.

I hope you will understand this matter.

Yours faithfully
P. Strauss

SITTING FOR POSTERITY

Editors' note: Beginning in 1969, Kasimir commissioned a series of portraits of his second dog, Anna Karenina II. Judging by the available evidence, they were based on sentimental Victorian scenes, often extolling heroism and other grand virtues. Unfortunately, only one finished example, And So She Swam, *survives. It is therefore of some consolation that Kasimir carefully kept a record of each set of artist's instructions. The finished canvas of* And So She Swam *measures 12" × 7". What happened to the remaining canvases is a mystery – as is the fact that each artist's brief includes instructions for a limited number of postcard-sized prints. Did he send these to friends and family? Nobody we contacted has ever seen one. We must assume that the series ends upon the death of Anna Karenina II.*

Brief for Artist
Date: 1 November 1969
Title: *And So She Swam*
Suggested detail: Anna she swim through towering sea with rope in mouth, towing lifeboat wherein cower survivors of shipwreck. On horizon is ship sinking in silhouette against storm cloud.

Special note: Anna is 'in season' and should be kept from male dogs and people in general.

Brief for Artist
Date: 1 November 1970
Title: *The Age of Steam*
Suggested detail: Anna sits in cabin of steam locomotive, head thrust into wind so ears are cast backwards. On head is colourful scarf, and on eyes, goggles.
Special note: Anna should be rewarded with spicy sausage for good behaviour.

Brief for Artist
Date: 1 November 1971
Title: *The New Girl*
Suggested detail: Anna stands on hind legs with hoop and bonnet, face of innocent apprehension at first day of schooling.
Special note: Anna will bite if provoked. Marjorie Petigrew will accompany Anna and oversee dressing in cape etc. Cape will be provided also.

Brief for Artist
Date: 1 November 1972
Title: *Jubilation!*
Suggested detail: London in Blitz: Nurse Anna has locate infant trap beneath rubble while Nazi Stuka plane burns in background. She will wear white hat of nurse and watch pinned to chest.
Special note: Anna does not like darkness.

Brief for Artist

Date: 1 November 1973

Title: *Apprehended!*

Suggested detail: In Victorian slum we see foul and filthy criminal lying in gutter while over his trembling frame Anna stand, in manner of Sherlock Holmes (or similar), with pipe and deerstalk as detail, having caught in act of criminal.

Special note: None.

Brief for Artist

Date: 1 November 1974

Title: *Bubbles*

Suggested detail: Anna is in garden of grand mansion blowing bubbles in manner of innocent child whiling hours away. After incident with bonnet three years ago, real bonnet will obvious not be use but perhaps artist will paint bonnet using sketch from previous sitting.

Special note: Anna is frightened of bubble also. Simulate bubble only during sitting (little balls from string?).

Brief for Artist

Date: 1 November 1975

Title: *The Prodigal Returns*

Suggested detail: Anna dressed in manner of hero back from quest, with tunic, sheath and sword detail. She will appear at end of dusty road, with gates in front of her.

Special note: None.

Brief for Artist
Date: 1 November 1976
Title: *Prudence*
Suggested detail: Anna, dress in apron, count money for
piggy bank.
Special note: Anna may eat coin, so great care to be
taken. Marjorie Petigrew will accompany Anna on each
time to study for evening class, psychology.

Brief for Artist
Date: 1 November 1977
Title: *Ho! The Armada!*
Suggested detail: As Spanish fleet approaches in distance
Anna stands on hind leg beside distract Drake, who
smoke pipe and does not notice ships. Anna point
towards ship, alerting all to danger.
Special note: Perhaps I shall pose for part of Drake.

Brief for Artist
Date: 1 November 1978
Title: *Faithful to the End*
Suggested detail: Dog lies with sad eyes on grave of
master. Clearly dog will die here, unable to leave side of
dead owner.
Special note: Anna has cold and must be wrap in blanket
when not in pose. I will accompany to artist studio
whenever possible.

THE MAGIC OF INVENTION

11 August 1992

Dear Uncle Kasimir,

The last time I saw you I must have been about five or six. I cannot actually remember meeting you at all but anyway, I'm called Sophia. I'm 20 and I live just outside Newcastle with my mum, in a village. I'm writing to you because I need some advice and my mum said that you are an inventor. She said that she has never met a businessman better than you, so maybe you can help me. She showed me a picture of you and Grandma Lottie from her album and told me about your lives during the war.

Do you like dogs? I expect so as there's one in the picture I saw. Is your dog still alive and what is he or she called? I am not allowed to have a dog in the house because Mum's allergic to them, but I am trying to work with dogs, so I can have my own dog business. I thought about all the dog businesses you could have and decided to start with dog walking. I don't know if you have dog walkers in Switzerland. They are people who will walk your dog for you if you are too busy, or too ill, or have to go to work all day. I put an advertisement in the Post

Office window and I got a few customers. The dogs I walked most often were called Benji, Anubis and Coco, who I loved, but they were really very badly behaved. Coco was probably the worst trained of the whole lot in one day she ran off in the park and trod in someone's picnic and also got her muddy paws on a womans white Capri pants (short trousers which are very fashionable) and peed in the doorway of a shop so this all gave me my BIG IDEA which was to become a dog trainer.

I made some new advertisements and booked a local hall to hold my classes. It was a bit of a 'white lie' but I said on the posters I was really experienced with dogs and, although there has been some problems like I had to ban an Alsatian which almost bit a poodle's leg completely off the classes are still going. The trouble is, even though I told that little lie on the posters I am very good at training dogs. You'd think this would be a good thing, but now almost all the dogs nearby are now trained and I can't find any more untrained ones. I don't know surely this doesn't always happen? There aren't even any other dog trainers round here, just me.

I thought of maybe designing dog products but all the ones I think of like the non-slip water bowl and the poop-scoop and etc. already exists. I just don't seem to be able to have any ideas but unless I do have some I will have to go on the dole.

Mum said that you are a wonderful business man and inventor and I know I would be such a good inventor of products if only I could think of one. I was also wondering, if it's not too much trouble, can you think of any ideas for me or can you give me some advice on how to have ideas? At the moment I only have two 'students' (dogs) to teach and am trying to make money selling watches on commission but I am not very good at this either. I have not sold any.

Yours sincerely,
Sophia

20 August 1992

Dearest Sophia,

Thank you for your letter. You do not ask if I am well. If you had ask I would tell you I am quite well despite recent influenza. You will be pleased to hear that while dog you witness in photo, Anna Karenina II, die several years ago (happily not in 'dog training' class) God has provided me with faithful new companion, Anna Karenina III. I have included small sketch of her I render at recent garden party. With regret I must confess that I do not remember you as child. In fact, of all your many cousins I only remember two: one wheezing, sickly child and small black-haired girl who tap-danced (she is now Gabi – do you know?). But this does not matter. For now you want to make your way in world as entrepreneur, and of this I approve. You are right when you say I am good businessman and inventor. I am, in fact, millionaire.

Many years before you were born, in 1941, there was siege of Leningrad. There, poodle leg would have been delicacy. In this siege I was trapped and I had to use head – not pinhead. Imagine, Sophia, city surrounded by enemy soldiers. No food can come in, no sick and hungry can go out. What would you do in this situation? How to survive? If you are hungry enough, you get ideas. If you have sniper pointing gun at your head, you get ideas. It is my life, harsh and long, that has taught me how to have ideas.

Perhaps to begin you should bear in mind following Polish wisdom: 'The roots of learning are bitter, but fruit is sweet.' This was told to me many times by my mother while she comfort me after intense instruction from my father, great military general. I have tasted sweet fruit on number of occasions but bitterness still runs through me like silt in clean water of River Warta. I did learn much about life from my father, of course but I also learn from estimable tutor hired by father, man by name of Blazej Kuss. With Kuss I learn important history, classic and of course Greek and Latin. But he also teach me to think like magician or escapologist, which is how great men must sometimes think (this, Kuss tell me). It is this think that you must learn if you are to solve your many problems, I am as sure of it as I am sure that God is in heaven and St Jude watch over us all.

Sophia, for some people mind is like plum tree in summer, ripe with precious fruit. But even healthy plum tree will carry bug. First plum of every season will

69

certainly carry bug, this my mother told me many years ago. Even your mother should know this fact. You would also know this if you did live in Poland, or nice retirement country like Switzerland but I imagine that in wasteland of 'Newcastle' there are few plum trees. Still, before you grow fruit, you must imagine fruit. And even when you have grow your fruit you will have to remove bug. But you cannot imagine or grow when you are, as you say, barren. Think of yourself therefore as plum stone, yet to be plant. Stone will learn and grow into beautiful tree bearing much fruit (with also bug, but we come to this later).

When I was mere plum stone, I went one day into schoolroom of old family home which would later be squat in by filthy Nazis. I could not see Blazej Kuss, estimable tutor, anywhere, yet I knew he was never late. I went to door and looked out and then, not seeing him in long, dusty corridor, turned back to the empty room. There he was! I still do not know how he achieve this illusion, but part of his family was from Hungary and related distant to Weiss family, so who can know? (Many from this family they move from Hungary to US in 1880, including great Harry Houdini, master of escapology and illusion, formerly Ehrich Weiss.) On this day, Kuss he declare that we will suspend normal lessons and learn something of escape, illusion and magic. I was completely thrilling, forgetting that such session would often con- clude with me tied and trapped in coffin, or similar. In this session, he simply set me following riddle. He say,

'Man is found dead in room which is lock from inside. There is pool of blood and pool of water on floor. A policeman immediately say, "The cause of death here is clear." How man die?' Kuss would not let me leave the room until I had solved this problem.

I have small task for you. You will solve this problem yourself and write me back the answer. If you do this, you will have taken first step not into world of magic, illusion and escapology (although these are similar) but into world of business. All problems are like magic illusion that can be solve, just as all of Houdini's many escapes are riddle with solutions we cannot see. Remember this.

Good luck, and may God be with you in all that you do,

Your Uncle Kasimir

1 September 1992

Dear Uncle Kasimir,

Thank you so much for writing back to me, I am sorry to hear about your recent flue. Are you feeling any better now? Thanks so much for sending me such a beautiful picture of Anna Karenina III. What a nice name. I have been working really hard, on your problem, and I really want to get it right but I haven't been getting on very well. I will keep trying though. Yesterday my two last students graduated and we had a little event in the hall, one little dog had come so far, that his owner actually cried when she thanked me.

Today I have been out trying to sell watches without any luck. It's so hard to do. You even have to learn a script. A woman called Angela drives two or three of us to a town centre and we split the shops up between us, then we have to go into the shops with a little case of these watches and say to the people working there 'Hi, look, I don't mean to be cheeky, but, I've just done a deal with a local jeweller on some watches, and I've got some left over. My boss says I can keep the left over ones as a commission but I don't need ten watches. They're really nice, though. They're very valuable. So I wondered if anyone here wanted to buy one at a vast reduction?'

Then I have to get out a copy of *Vogue* (a magazine) from about three years ago and show the people in the shop the advert on the back. I carry on by saying 'Do you know the magazine *Vogue*, well, these watches have even been advertised there. Look.' I show them the ad. 'Now, I've been selling these watches for a hundred pounds each, to a jeweller, who is going to mark them up to £166.99 but I'd be willing to let these ones go for say £70 each.' Our boss says he only wants £20 per watch. Whatever we can sell them for above that is ours to keep. Angela always sells about ten a day but I can't get it at all. This should be funding my other business ideas but it isn't at all. They said you could earn so much doing it like Angela does, and they say I can sell the watches in whichever way I want, but Angela says here is the best way.

I really want to have an idea for a dog product. I don't like watches, and I don't like talking to people in shops. But what's the alternative? Everything is so difficult. This evening, just before I sat down to write this letter, I went to the park and I noticed someone throwing a toy for his dog. It was a ball on a short piece of rope with a knot in the end. It was easy to throw and the dog seemed to love it, why didn't I have this idea?

Any handy hints on the 'dead man problem' would be really appreciated.

Yours sincerely,
Sophia

7 September 1992

Dearest Sophia,

I am quite well now and not at all ailing by recent influenza. Pilates, set of exercises invented by German (but, I suspect, stolen from Pole), keep me in good health. Anna Karenina is out fishing at this moment, on edge of garden pond. All day she sit there with recent obsession, trying to use paw as bait and line. I tell her this is not how to catch fish but she has misconstruction of great biologist Charles Darwin, and does expect to evolve 'fishing' ability before she die. She say to me, 'I have seen cat do this.' I tell her, 'You are not cat,' but she does not listen. And in same manner our lives will go on, with grace of God.

You tell me in your letter that everything is 'difficult'. Perhaps I should tell you something about difficult. In 1943 I was incarcerate in French prison camp from which, like great Houdini, I effect miracle escape with only small pin and grace of God (Kuss taught me much about escape). After this I need to cross Pyrenees through underground resistance network. I was in safe house with three others, about one hundred miles from mountain pass. Here were two British officers who also had escape from nearby prison camp, and female radio operator from resistance, who had been betray and so was returning to England. In safe house we were fed and bathed and giving false papers. We were all to pose as French on train journey to next safe house on route.

On train we all sat separate in same carriage, fear for our lives. It was risk strategy as, of four of us, just two spoke fluent French: myself, of course, and resistance woman, 'Little Owl', educate in France before war. It was she who realise that Gestapo were on train, not just checking papers but looking for 'three British spy and one escape Pole'. We had been betray and could not go to next safe house on route, as this would also probably now be known by Gestapo.

We see Nazi approaching carriage and move like swift down the train, where we waited only a few seconds before jumping to land in field of cows. Gestapo see us and start firing but we did only receive minor flesh wounds as we ran for cover across field. Soon we came upon small farmhouse which we creep around, unknowing if inside would be friend or collaborator. Then one officer he beckon to me and tell me to listen against window. Inside, radio was on and it was clearly BBC. We take chance and knock. We explain to farmer and wife what is happening and that we need escape from area, as Germans see us jump from train. Farmer gave us car and map and tell us to go quickly with grace of God. Farmer's wife bandage our wounds, give us sandwiches and also small can of petrol.

We drive fast down country roads, British officer trying to remember to drive on right-hand side. Then we approach Nazi checkpoint. What should we do? We have no disguise and were fitting to description of abscond traitors exactly. We turn off down small farm track on edge of ravine to study map and try to find alternate route. But then, disaster. One tyre it hit rock and bursts. We pull over to side of ravine and British officer unbolt wheel. But he is pinhead and arrange four wheel nuts so precise on to sides that each four roll down small hill into ravine, lost for ever, like childhood in wartime.

The rest of us curse him and call him pinhead but it is too late. We are now four escapee with car with only three wheel. Other officer put head in hands and declare, with 'chin-up' English voice, 'Well, chaps, looks like doom, eh?'

First officer start to cry.

But I remember lessons of Blazej Kuss.

'Get out spare tyre,' I tell pathetic weeping officer. 'We have all we need to fix it on.'

'Are you going to do it with grass?' Little Owl ask, her eyes big like true owl. 'Or fashion something from rock?'

'I will fix wheel,' I say with confidence.

'There really is nothing we can do, Czerniak,' says first officer. 'We have spare tyre but no wheel nuts to affix. We must make run for it now. Get into the woods before darkness falls.'

But, Sophia, we indeed have all we needed to fix wheel there and then. Can you think what I did? I will tell you. I take one nut from each other wheel and fix spare tyre with these. Now each wheel only has three nut, but this is better than for three wheel to have four and for one wheel to have nothing. Do you think it is amazing that British officer did not see this? I am myself amazed at how many people look but do not see.

You have to look at problem in new way if you want to solve. Einstein, European genius and inventor of possibility for time travel, say, 'We cannot solve problem with same level of thinking that create them.' He is right. I agree with you that you must come up with product invention soon. You are not good for this selling of watch. You must like what you sell or how will you convince others also to like and, indeed, desire? Perhaps this woman Angela like these watch and it is why she is able to sell. I guess that she write this script, yes? That is why it works for her. You must write own script.

Meanwhile I have further task for you. Go to park again and watch people with dogs. Pretend you are soldier filing reconnaissance report to superior officer about the habit and custom of these dog-walker. Perhaps your army is aiming to infiltrate this park and needs to know customs of inhabitants. What do the people do? What do dogs do? Look with new eyes and see. Send this report to me by next week and then we see what to do next.

May God be with you in all that you do.

Your Uncle Kasimir

15 September 1992

Dear Uncle Kasimir,

I have done as you asked and here is my report of what I saw.

Dogs seem to be brought to the park for 3 reasons,
1) to go to the toilet,
2) to run around and get some exercise,
3) to meet other dogs, which is good for them.

I noticed that people bring some things with them to help them and they bring toys for their dogs to fetch including balls, and frisbees. They bring carrier bags, to clear up after their pets (not doing this carries a maximum penalty of £1000, it says, signs all over the park). Most people use recycled supermarket carrier bags. Some people use scented 'nappy sacks', in case the smell is quite bad. I didn't see anyone use the 'poop-scoop' on sale in most pet shops, (I'm glad I didn't have that idea!). One woman had so many carrier bags in her pocket that they kept falling out, and she had to stuff them back in her pockets all of the time.

People wear waterproof or 'outdoor' clothing for dog-walking. At the end of their walk, many of the dogs go in the back of their owners cars because they were wet or filthy, some people had brought along towels to dry their dogs.

<u>This is the end of my report.</u>

Is this the right sort of thing? I hope so. I am still trying to work out the dead man's puzzle, and I still haven't sold any watches.

Yours faithfully,
Sophia

21 September 1992

Dear Uncle Kasimir,

I don't know if you got my last letter as you haven't replied, I got excited the other day as I thought a letter had finally arrived from you, but it turned out to be for Mum, not me. Anyway, I thought I'd let you know my news. I have sold two watches! Since you didn't reply so quickly this time I read your other letters again. I have thought a lot about your story about the car tyre and I think that maybe you are trying to tell me that I have all the answers already. I also thought about Angela's script and you were right! She did write the script and it suits her personality, but not mine . . . you are also right that I do not like these watches. I don't even believe they are worth £70, so I am not going to be able to sell them for that. I know I probably should have left the job then and there but then I thought about all the things you said, so I decided to treat this more like a puzzle, and then I remembered what you said about Houdini's tricks being like puzzles. I got a book about him, out of the library in Newcastle.

I read all about his famous tricks and how he would also write a 'script' (like Angela's) to tell to the audience to make them believe what he wanted them to believe as Magical Tricks depends on the audience not seeing what you are really doing. Before some of his famous escapes Houdini would take his clothes off and get searched for lock picks and he relied on the searchers and the audience not thinking to look in places like his hair, under the skin on the souls of his feet and in his mouth e.g. they would look but not see!

Many people still don't know how Houdini did his tricks but in this book it told about some early tricks he used to perform with his wife, called Bess. One simple one was a mind-reading trick where his wife would look at a number like on a dollar bill or something from the audience and then send it to Houdini by telepathy. She would say things to him, as she sent it with the power of her mind. She'd say things like: 'Tell me, mind-reader. Look into your heart. Say, can you answer me, pray?' And then he would recite back the correct number, if I saw this performed, I would think it was amazing and would not be able to work out how it was done. But the book gave the answer. It said that the Houdinis worked out a code beforehand and the word 'pray' meant the number 1 and the word 'answer' meant the number 2 and Bess would arrange the words into sentences that would tell Houdini what the numbers were. Seeing as there are only ten digits only ten words need to be memorised.

Anyway, the day after I'd read the Houdini's book I got up early and bought a book of cloakroom tickets. I thought, I am never going to sell these watches in a million years, so why don't I raffle them off instead, and it was just like you said e,g. seeing instead of looking. I knew I could not sell the watches but I could sell tickets for a raffle with watches as a prize, I decided to raffle one man's and one womens' watch together as a set. I sold the tickets for £1.50 each. By the end of the day I had sold a hundred tickets, I worked out that although I didn't believe the watches were worth £70 I knew a set was a bargain for £1.50. So I had no problem persuading other people. I have a profit of £110, minus £1.20 for the cloakroom tickets. I can invest this in my dog invention, if only I had one! But I am working on that problem and also the 'dead man' problem, I have realised that the man must have been cut or stabbed because of the blood but I don't see how it could have happened. I will keep working on it.

Yours faithfully,
Sophia

1 October 1992

Dearest Sophia,

So I go away for few days to beneficial spa in mountains and come back to find that you are using head in business and even giving self help in most difficult mind-bending problem. This is impressive. And you are reading about great Houdini, too. Perhaps you have also the time to read over report that you made in park? This will help you. Now that you have money to invest you are in ideal position to design product. But which product will you choose? Only you can decide.

When I first came to Great Britain in 1945 all I have was clothing on my back and pencil I find beneath shrine of St Jude – far less than case of watches. But with one pencil man can make picture of his own good fortune. During the war I study English because I hear Churchill speak that he will fight the Germans on beaches. I saw that this was language of future and it is so, would you not say? When I reach England at Dover I take copy of local newspaper from bin to read financial news – only I see prize crossword first. I complete crossword, take to newspaper office and collect first prize: five pounds. With one pound I buy smart shoes to replace pair I lose in siege of Leningrad (long story), and then I go to river. I have German grenade conceal in trousers since Holland, and with this I exploded river and kill many salmon. For four pounds I purchase black market sack and ice from fishing market and transport best salmon to top Hotel in London. This salmon they buy under counter for fifty pounds. Like you, I feel rich.

What to do with fifty pounds? This was problem similar to yours, although different. All around me, people make business from detritus of war. Black market did continue to thrive in time of ration and people even sell off surplus from army: heavy boot, canvas bags and ration tins. I need to invest my money in something I could sell for profit and of course enjoy to sell for profit. Of course, like you, I want really to be great inventor (and I am now, of course, inventor, although not great, but millionaire still). But I need to sell for profit to make money to invest in patent etc. As you see with watch, it is difficult to sell items which you are believing have little value (although your solution to this problem it is admirable). But what did people buy after war? I will tell you what they buy. Fantasy and illusion of the cinema and theatre. Yes, my dear Sophia, I see many new acts emerge in this time – acts of daring and magic. I think back to estimable tutor, Kuss, and decide to invest some of my money in illusions. Perhaps you will not understand what this is. In faraway days of 'post-war' and even before this, before even my own childhood, magician they would often sell secret and detail of illusions. Houdini himself once try to sell his Metamorphosis Substitution, where he exchange place with wife while he is in bag locked in trunk, and she behind curtain; and Hindoo Needle Trick, taught to him by Hindus at World's Fair in 1893, in which great man would swallow up to 50 sewing needle and some thread and then vomit needles connected to thread. No one bought these illusions, even though Hindoo Needle Trick was offer for only five dollar. I start to examine *Stage* magazine and similar organ. I come upon several illusions for sale. But instead of buying these and presenting them on stage myself I buy illusions and improve them. Then, in few years, I plan to sell for large profit. On this I spend £25. On board and food I spend £5.

Long-term speculation it only works in long term, of course, and I need income in short term also. With remaining twenty pounds I go to exploded theatres, shops and museums looking for items to buy and later sell. Many people have same idea. In fact, many times I arrive at bomb site and find nothing remain, as if place was corpse strip by vulture. On one occasion I arrive at auction of effects of Palace Theatre to find nothing but old blackening curtains. Even planks of wood from stage were gone. Auctioneer was packing up briefcase and placing hat on head as if all business was in conclusion. So I make him offer for curtains. He was full of surprise. Perhaps people are so used to seeing curtains in theatre that they do not see them. They look, but do not see. So I take curtains away. These I wash, brush down and repair and then sell to cinema. I visit more auctions and buy more curtains which I sell to other cinemas and theatres for immediate profit.

In business as in world of illusion you must see what other people do not see. This you are now learning. It is like joke: punch it seem obvious only when you hear it. So now you must look back to park scene. What can you see there that others do not?

Good luck and may God be with you in all that you do.

Uncle Kasimir

14 October 1992

Dear Uncle Kasimir,

The man stabbed himself with a dagger made of ice, is that the answer?

Sorry, I am in such a hurry that I have almost forgotten to ask if you are well, I hope you are and that Anna Karenina III is still enjoying her fishing, anyway, I have some brilliant news! All your advice has helped me so much that I now have a dog invention. I am selling it as well. I did as you said and looked back over the notes I made. It was such a good idea of yours to make notes because I had a record of things I wouldn't normally notice. To be honest, on the day I did it I wasn't to sure what I should write so I was just writing any old things, so I read back the bit about the carrier bags and I remembered what a pain it used to be when I did dog-walking and pockets full of plastic bags bulging everywhere. I wondered again why people didn't use poop-scoops but I realised that nobody actually wants to use a scoop – instead people would probably like a device that bags can be stored in, to stop them expanding in your pockets etc. etc. I did some experiments and found that while it is only possible to fit 1 or 2 scrunched up carrier bags in one pocket, if you have a box or a tin that will fit in the same pocket you can squash as many as five bags into the tin and the bags will not expand.

Next, I found the name of a manufacturer of tins. I found out that this manufacturer made mainly tobacco tins, with pictures of tobacco leaves on them and got a quote for him to make up a hundred tins with 'I LOVE MY DOG' on them. He said he would do it for £100 including VAT. I thought this was a bit expensive but I had the tins made anyway, then I bought two bumper bags of nappy sacks and stuffed each tin with five or six of them. I decided that I would sell the tins 'pre-packed' in this way, and demonstrate to people that they could easily restock the tins with their own bags.

I decided that the best place to sell my product would be in the place where people encountered the problem, so

I set up a little stall in the Oaklands car park during lunchtimes and between six and seven, when most people walk their dogs, I also realised that people who had forgotten to bring any bags at all would be attracted to the idea of avoiding a £1000 fine and would like being able to buy bags 'on the spot' and I priced each tin at £3.

And you'll never guess what else I did. As a 'special offer' I gave away a raffle ticket with each tin sold, the prize being yes a set of his'n'hers watches! So I am 'selling' watches <u>and</u> my dog tins, in my first week I sold all hundred tins! And I am only drawing the raffle once a week so, for an outlay of £20 (watches) and £100 (tins) and approx £2 (nappy sacks) I have made a total of £300. That's a profit of £178! Needless to say I will spend this profit on more tins although I will try to get the manufacturer to drop his price this time, now when Angela drops us off in a town centre, I will make straight for the park, with my tins and my raffle tickets while the others stick to the shops.

What do you think? Maybe even Houdini would have been impressed!

Yours sincerely,
your loving niece
Sophia

A NEW HOUSE

21 June 1969

My Dear Lizzie,

I hope that the dust has begun to settle in your new home in Faversham. With Alec so close – Tanner Street is merely ten minute walk from your front door – I know that I need not worry about you. Please, make a good life with young Adam and think nothing of what you call my 'generosity'. I say, as my father say, 'What is in the family, is in the family.'

So all that I ask is for you to place a candle at the holy shrine of St Jude, please, in memory of my health. A small thing, but I trust that you will endulge me. Very soon I will come to visit you – perhaps I will share with you some of the work I have been doing (with a pen!).

All of my love
Uncle Kasimir

THE PRISONER'S DILEMMA
A Talk for the Students of Class 4E,
——— School, Faversham

Editors' note: This is an interesting document. It's unlikely that anyone in our family would have suggested Kasimir should give such a talk to a class of schoolchildren – the likelihood that he might inadvertently frighten or confuse some of the more timid children would have prevented that. Kasimir never suffered fools gladly, even little ones. Instead we believe he might have suggested giving the talk himself, perhaps after having met a member of the school staff while visiting a relative in Faversham. Unfortunately we could find no record of the outcome.

Many times I have been asked about decision-making. It is true that in my life I have often faced dilemmas with no easy solution. Take this example: during the war I was for a time confined to monastic cell in mountain of Italy with septicaemia of right arm. This I obtained from dangerous mountain snakebite while climbing vertical cliff wall to reach monastery. Why did I not simply use mountain road winding from valley to heights of this monastery? Because at bottom of the road was enemy encampment to guard this mountain pass. By climbing to the monastery I hope to hurl rocks and create avalanche to crush Nazis. This was possible – a trick told to me many times by my father, great military general, who route one hundred insurgent of Carpathian mountains simply by kicking one pebble from mountain top.

Unfortunately, because of snake I collapse at monastery and was too sick (at door of death) either to throw rocks or to climb down. I ask holy brethren of monk to throw me from monastery walls on to Nazis, but this they refuse and made vow instead to heal me. For this I was grateful and for several days I lie recovering in a monk cell.

Then, disaster. I am discover by ignorant, Godless Nazi searching cells for supply of wine. At once he guess wrong that I am resistance fighter because of captured Nazi pistol I keep beside bed. I was of course officer of Polish Army.

He drag me from bed and tie me to washing-post in middle of monastery courtyard beneath blazing midday sun. I guess at once he did plan to extract information. Not only I but every monk know location of large resistance camp hidden deep in mountain caves, and so this was problem.

On post beside me he tied Abbot of monastery, venerable old man with long beard who speak no German. In fact, he speak nothing at all because of vow of silence.

'You will tell me,' German say to Abbot in poor French, assuming with profound stupid that Italian monk might speak French, 'where this man came from or I will shoot every one of monks.' Old Abbot could not speak French and had anyway made vow of silence. He shrug and nod to one of other monks.

Other monk speak no French either.

'Do you know any Latin?' I insolently ask Nazi in perfect French. I then repeat same in German to impress on him my superior intelligence.

Nazi he whip me with pistol, a petty gesture so mild in comparison to instructional beatings I have receive from my father. He then shoot foot off statue to holy martyr St Sebastian and laugh like jackal. The brethren look on aghast.

He whip me again and say to me: 'What is your name?'

I tell him immediately: 'Kazimierz Czerniak.' And then I add: 'Son of great military general.' I spit at his feet. He step back at once and regard me with full trepidation. He not bargain on encountering son of great and famous military general Stanisław Czerniak.

'I see. You are soldier, then.'

I nod. 'I am an officer of Polish Army.' As such I was protect by Geneva Convention and, moreover, to murder son of Stanisław Czerniak would be no easy thing to do.

He raise pistol and point barrel directly at my head. 'You do, however, know of location of resistance camp,' he to me. 'You will give information and then I will take you prisoner.' I notice severe trembling of his hand as barrel of gun waver like stalk of wheat on windswept field.

I spit on ground and he cock hammer of pistol.

He spoke to me in German, which Abbot could not understand. 'We will play interesting game,' say cruel and inhuman Nazi, with revive spirit. 'I will ask you first where resistance hiding place is. Then I will ask Abbot. You will translate. You can choose to lie, tell truth or remain silent. If you both tell me where resistance hiding place is, and you tell me same place, you will both go free – although resistance camp will be exploded. If one of you remain silent and other tells – the silent one will be shot, the one who spoke will go free and the resistance camp will be exploded. If you both tell of different locations, I will explore both, and then return to shoot liar. Then resistance camp will be exploded. Truth-teller will go free. If you both remain silent, you will both be shot, but resistance camp will not be exploded unless I find by accident. Do you understand?'

I nod. I understand that this is difficult game indeed. One of his soldiers took Abbot away while I deliberate on how to answer puzzle.

What would you do in this situation? How do you work out best strategy? Is best strategy to make sure you yourself go free or not?

It was only much later that I realise dilemma I was face on mountain top it is twisting version of classic Prisoner's Dilemma puzzle – also philosophical conundrum. Classic version is simpler than one concocted by Nazi: two criminal accomplices have been captured by polices. The polices do not have evidence to convict these criminals and so must try other method to seek confession. My father, great military general, could have taught polices something of taking confession from prisoners but these polices do not wish to use torture, they use brain instead. They separate prisoners and give both same proposition. Police say to each criminal: 'If you confess and accomplice remain silent, you will go free and he will go to prison for ten years. If both of you remain silent, you will each get six months in prison. If both of you confess, you will each get five years.'

Perhaps he drew diagram to make it easier for pin-headed criminals to understand. (DRAW DIAGRAM ON BLACKBOARD IN CHALK):

	You silent	You confess
Comrade silent	6 months each	He go prison for ten years, you go free
Comrade confess	You go prison for ten years and comrade he go free	Five years each

What will these criminals do? If one wants to maximum his own chance of freedom, and cares not about betraying the other, he should confess, hoping that other stays silent. But if both do this, both will go to prison for five years (which is indeed short sentence of betrayal). The most clever thing to do would be for both criminals to remain silent. But, of course, in harsh and bitter world of puzzle (and life beyond), silence can send you to prison for ten years, if accomplice he confess. Since neither criminal know what other has done, it is impossible to judge correct. It bring to mind famous Polish proverb, 'Better to lose with wise man than to win with fool.'

When I learn of this puzzle, it was during time of post-war optimist and 'baby-boom'. People were often speaking of banning bomb and embracing 'love and peace'. People say that humanity should embrace equivalent of 'silence' from puzzle and all make small sacrifice for greater common good. Western women would not shave armpit any more! Things would be recycled, as in Poland. In this way, we in England and US imagined we would be able to colonise space before Russians (who were still practise on beloved motherland). On smaller level, imagine water shortage. Does everyone rush to river (or supermarket) and take more than they are needing, leaving nothing for latecomers? Or does everyone simply take what they need and no more and leave enough for everyone? It is all conundrum indeed.

It is also so in prisoner's dilemma. The best result for 'group' (you and other criminal) is for six months each. Together, that is total of only one year in prison. All other outcome end in ten years in prison altogether. But to stay silent hoping friend will have logic and loyalty enough to do some is to also gamble with possibility of serving ten years while he go free. And of course, for some weak, pathetic people, six months in prison is too much for spirit to bear. So much so that they would send comrade to prison for ten years in order to avoid.

What can we learn from this? Several things (WRITE ON BLACKBOARD IN CHALK):

1 Do not commit crime in first place.
2 If you must commit crime, work alone and do not get caught.
3 Learn escapology at early age. (Tell class about friend Wojek who used to get mother to bind him in chains and lock him in coffin and then push over side of River Warta, princess of Polish rivers.)
4 Remember that he who digs pits under others falls into them himself.
5 Understand that there is no answer to Prisoner's Dilemma.
6 Understand also that the only solution to the Prisoner's Dilemma is if the rules are changed and you can *talk* to your comrade. (Tell students: can this be apply to life in any way? Think of situations where communication could help against common enemy. If you work for company, tell your colleagues what you are paid. Ask them to tell you what they are paid. If you find out that janitor is paid three times more than you, and you are, say, salesman, you can remedy. Boss will be hoping you simply never find out.)

As I stood there in grounds of monastery, I did not know any of this. However, instinct told me to remain silent. The resistance must survive, for greater good of humanity! I am businessman, true, and in business one must sometimes be selfish. But more often one must consider wider situation. It is in this way that one becomes millionaire, rather than market trader. Do not ask me how.

'Very well,' say Nazi scum. 'Now I will bring Abbot back and you will explain proposition to him in Latin.'

Abbot was brought back. In Latin I explain to him Nazi proposition. I also tell him my choice – it is not as if ignorant Nazi knew what I was saying. Abbot also remains silent. Whether this is vow or decision I do not know. So, there we stood: dead men, condemned men. We wait to be shot.

'Have your way then,' say Nazi. He aim gun at Abbot head first. With wry smile, he pull trigger of pistol and the hammer click. But no shot was fire. Instead small bird start to sing on top of cripple statue of St Sebastian. Above us, sun slip behind dark cloud. In the distance, thunder which sound like faint laughter of gods.

Abbot spoke, breaking vow of silence with perfect German: 'It is miracle.'

At this Nazi's face it fill with fear and he run in terror from monastery. Monks escape with me through secret catacomb to far side of mountain where they join with the resistance.

But miracle had not yet achieved conclusion. Seeking revenge vile Nazis blow up monastery. Had they known military history they might have been familiar with Carpathian victory of my own father – but they were not and ensuing rock fall did crush every one of Germans in valley below.

PAVING STONES (FAVERSHAM)

14 January 1972

My dear Alec,

I am so sorry to hear about your fall. I trust that lovely Helia will be able to cope with your desolate mood, which I detected in our last telephone conversation – and which I expect will only be alleviated by a visit from your little brother. Typically, however, I am at present detained in London by affairs, and the car is in pieces at garage (big end gone). Although Faversham is but a short journey from London, it may well not be for a week or two that I can visit you.

In my absence I suggest that you obtain good legal representation in order to sew local council. This is a nation of loose paving stones and in view of Marxist agitation (ie Scargill, etc) I am firmly of an opinion that these will simply become looser.

Marjorie is sending you her love, also. To which I add mine, my brother.

Yours most truly,
Kasimir

LONDON TO EDINBURGH: CHICKEN

The editors disagree regarding the exact purpose of this document. Recorded in similar fashion to the 'Surveillance' notes (see pp. 194–9 and 209–11), but fortunately in far better condition than those rather obscure observations, it is a collection of notes taken at eating establishments on the road between London and Edinburgh during the mid-1960s. Most are on the M1 and A1, but a few off the main routes. General comments scattered throughout the piece make it easy to date approximately, but Kasimir seems to have experimented with a coded naming/dating mechanism that neither of us has been able to decipher. Naturally we have presented this for your puzzlement.

Perhaps Kasimir had aspirations towards being a food critic – his literary ambitions are widely chronicled throughout this collection. Alternatively, there may be a more unusual motive: in the light of the 'Surveillance' pieces, we feel this should not be discounted. Kasimir was always excited by new technology; maybe he simply enjoyed cruising along the nation's new motorways, marvelling at the space-age architecture. It could be argued that the food – even the chicken – was secondary to his interest in the buildings but the chicken is surely important. Throughout, it is as if Kasimir has a point to prove regarding chicken. That is why we have mentioned the bird in the title.

Doncaster: Mr Kippy
Chicken with a smell

A fine establishment from outside, but only superficially so. This prestigious appearance is less so when viewed from pavement on other side of this street. Up close, one is drawn to overwhelming glamour of MR KIPPY, neon sign of some taste. From other side of street this magpie-ruse is dispelled by a view of restaurant's neighbours: HORACE ASQUITH CARPETS (to left) and MERRY THOUGHT PETS (to right). So, a hum-drum setting.

But what of the food?

My guest for this evening, Mrs Petigrew, and I both ordered chicken. For my part I asked the waiter (swarthy Italian, I believe, with an easy manner and ready smile – too ready?) to ensure that my bird was not overcooked. Mrs Petigrew was not specific, being already distracted by a smell. At this time (6.45 p.m.) we were single clientele, so this smell was a mystery, but to this I will return.

Our meal arrived very quickly – too fast, in fact. One minute and nine seconds according to my timepiece (Swiss). 'This is freshly prepared?' I asked Italian. 'But of course, sir,' he say, although with an oily tone.

'And what of this smell?' asked Mrs Petigrew.

'I can smell nothing,' said Italian, twitching nose like mouse (and a guilty mouse, one who has stolen the cheese).

I tasted chicken as our waiter retreated, talking in his native tongue and was appalled to discover our meal was inedible. Accompanying vegetables were soft like fudge and sauce was not fit for dog bowl, let alone my table.

I call back waiter and accused him point blank of serving us overcooked nonsense which had lain on stove since lunchtime. As Mrs Petigrew pointed out, her chicken was as dry as Egyptian Mummy, or dead parrot from next door (MERRY THOUGHT PETS).

Italian told us why we insult him. So I mentioned to him: 'My friend, you would do well to remember your manners in front of a lady.' And of course I informed him of what would follow.

Our host did weep and offer me substantial compensation for my time and travel.

This is an establishment we will not be visiting again. Beware of Mr Kippy, Doncaster.

Scotch Corner: Pringle's Rocket
Chicken like a surface of the moon
My older brother Alec say that this restaurant, easily accessible from A1, has best lavatory in Britain. As frequent traveller, he is a man to know. 'But what of the restaurant facilities?' I ask him before my visit. 'My good lady wife Helia and I travel with sandwiches,' he told me. 'It is a better alternative to remain in own

vehicle and eat that which you know than to venture by necessity into a strange kitchen. Lavatory is, however, quite out of our world.'

This is, I must stress, a most futuristic experience. The kind of thing I believe typical English diner would not believe could contain a meal – such as I have see their fondness for Inglenook and similar. Approaching Pringle's Rocket is like venturing upon Cape Canaveral, and more so, as if I were lonely peasant of Ukraine glimpsing capitalistic majesty for the first time. Atop glittering dome is, in resemblance of crescent moon, a great chip (a potato chip) – maybe twenty feet in height. And this chip is studded like cowboy trousers with rhinestone, quite amazing lighting effect. On plinth outside restaurant door, which is great curved metal artefact combining slats, not unlike roller blind which open sideways, is Pringle Rocket itself. How may I describe this? According to plaque affixed underneath rocket fin, proprietor Mr Pringle (highly successful businessman) has since youth nurtured an ambition to stand upon the moon. Towards this worthy goal he has devoted much time and great expense supporting rocket research at nearby Darlington College of Technology.

My guest for the evening was, once more, Mrs Petigrew. We installed ourselves at marvelous table, like table might perhaps be in spaceship, and young woman waitress approached us wearing 'cosmic' suit.

'Hey, daddyo,' she said to me, or similar. I smile, but Marjorie gave both myself and this woman a fierce look, directing my attention to waitress's short sleek and silver skirt, like vole. Now, in normal circumstance I would regard such an outfit as quite wrong for one in public service (unless in certain bars and establishments, gentlemen's clubs customary in central London and so on, etc), but being aware of latest trends not only culturally but in Science Fiction, her outfit seemed suitable.

Quietly, we order chicken.

Once this waitress had departed I broke ice by asking Mrs Petigrew for her thoughts on the potential of life to be found elsewhere in our universe. As former headmistress of girls' school, I was certain she might hold a view on this.

'I am a firm believer in the extra-terrestrials,' she said to me, pondering a range of substantial artworks hanging around us on the walls (artistic representations of alien beings, spaceship and celestial body). 'And I think such life would have great potential.'

'So you believe that life may exist beyond the stars?' I ask her.

'Of course.' This surprise me enormously. Great is my affection for Marjorie, but I have always imagined (wrongly, it appears) her soul to have a much greater inclination towards poetry than prose.

At any rate, our chicken arrive: large breast for each of us, with antenna implanted close to bone.

'Should this be withdrawn?' asked Marjorie, twiddling aerial. 'Surely one might choke on such an appendage?'

I called back our waitress and in a polite manner suggested to her the fault we had found in our space-age chicken.

'This aerial is dangerous,' I stated. At this precise same moment Marjorie partook of her chicken, and made to me an expression as if she had bitten on her own limb.

'Good grief,' she remarked. 'This chicken is dry like sawdust.'

I took my own mouthful and promptly spat the meat back on to a hastily arranged napkin. 'This is not chicken,' I say. 'This is like a wall.'

'Like a wall?' ask the waitress.

'Like plaster dust of wall,' I clarified. 'Or paint flake.'

'Or,' said Marjorie, making a play with the aerial, 'like surface of the moon.'

The waitress did not take kindly to this. In fact she weep profoundly, sobbing as if she was beaten or scolded (as if servant girl from kitchen of my youth, which I see on occasion).

'It is all very well for you to shed tears,' said Marjorie, 'but in my mind it is the customer who should weep.'

Again, I would counsel against Pringle's Rocket. One more establishment to erase from our copious list. Although the ambience may be overwhelming the food is equally overdone.

Woolfox: Night Owl
A slaughterhouse, not a restaurant
The Night Owl café in Woolfox is a humble establish-

ment with a simple menu targeting the long-distance lorry driver, travelling salesman or similar. Towards this end, on my arrival – I park behind lengthy lorry carrying brick – I proceed to the sturdy cabin and make my choice from three principle items. On this occasion I am on my own, my companion Marjorie having expressed unease at the habits of working men (such as lorry drivers, etc).

The first principle item is a sausage with garnish and either bread slices (to make sandwich, with sauce) or potato chips, fried. I ask gentleman standing behind long shiny counter – I note that this is at first sight a clean place – what type of sausage he has on offer for the evening.

'Meat,' comes forth reply, and I assess his gaze to see whether he is making light of me. But no, there is a deadness behind this man's eyes, his face somewhat bovine, which suggests to me that his answer is an honest one. I am left to muse among myself as to what kind of meat.

The second principle item is a soup – on this occasion an oxtail with a white roll. I peruse the steaming basin of soup on the stove and find it does nothing for my palate, although the scent of ox is strong.

The third principle item is whole chicken.

'My man,' I say in casual manner reminiscent of the type of clientele normally passing through these where-abouts, 'one chicken please.'

'To go?' he ask.

'Indeed,' I say.

He remove himself from my vision to a store of some sort and returned with a steaming bird.

'Is this a fresh chicken?' I ask, eyeing carcass suspiciously.

'Fresh?' He gaped at me like a fish from a aquarium. Clearly he have no concept of my question. 'Fresh kill or freshly prepared?' he asked.

'Indeed,' I say. 'Whichever.'

'Both,' was his reply, starting to wrap this chicken in a white bag. 'Round back.'

'Round back?'

'Aye' – like a sailor – 'the governor does the birds round the back on his slate, fresh off the truck. Then he pluck them.'

'Out back?'

'No, back there.' He point towards a cubby hole with a half-door.

'Is this hygienic?' I ask.

'Search me,' says the man, who I now assume to be a muttonhead.

'That will not be required,' I tell him, turning on my heels.

'But your chicken, mate,' he call after me.

'Keep it. I prefer to dine in restaurant, however humble. Not slaughterhouse.'

'Suit yourself,' he say, no doubt unwrapping chicken to foist on the next punter.

I will suit myself. Avoid at any cost this barbaric lavatory which is unfit to serve a chip, let alone a chicken.

NEWCASTLE

1 August 1978

My dearest Ola,

It was such a pleasure to see both you and your lovely little girl, and of course young Adam, a fine man. Newcastle both agrees and disagrees with me, like, after a fashion, the way your father Max sing (as he did for us on last night of my visit).

Please, say 'Cuckoo!' to little Sophie and give her one little kiss on the head from her Uncle Kasimir. No doubt as she grows up into a beautiful woman (just so like her mother, I imagine), I will be delighted to introduce her to a world of culture and, perhaps warmer climes!

One thing that I remember: in manner, your father reminds me a little of my old acquaintance Captain Lasiewicz, who our family call Lasi, once great leader of military regiment but who suffered from a sick head following bombing. You know, I never notice this before. You should mention this to your mother Lotta, because she always enjoy the merry spirited company of Lasi, especially in autumn when he did spend many hours turning over our garden for approaching winter. Lasi was many things to us, including family gardener and idiot-philosopher (which I say out of great respect).

However, my point in mentioning this is that, perhaps, your mother became a love for your father out of misty-eye memory of old Lasi and his strange ways, often in nature.

I enjoy a variety of things in Newcastle, for example the bridge and some fog – which was extremely melancholic. No doubt this city of coal has doughty heart and will offer up to you much happiness (although damp!) in the future.

All of my love,
Uncle Kasimir

THE MULTIDIMENSIONAL
WRISTWATCH

*(Editors' note: Kasimir made many successful patent
applications. However, in his chest we found several
patent-style documents with a different tone from
those that were officially filed. We do not know
what he meant to do with them. Though they
follow the standard format for patent applications
they are eccentric, to say the least. Also, his English
is poorer in these earlier documents, although still,
we believe, perfectly understandable.)*

Abstract
Date: 27 January 1951
I have firm belief that there exists further dimensions of
time beyond the one we have currently experience. Is time
simply line, on which humans are trap to spend all of
existence gloomy marching forward with no chance to
turn left or right, as condemned soldier on bridge of twig?
Is time prison, like Nazi camp, which have only one
entrance, and at end, death? No. This cannot be so. Fabric
of bendy space time it contain wormhole, and wormhole is
hole not for worm but for human wishing to turn left or
right (or up or down or perhaps into 4th, 5th and Nth
dimension) from the line of time and experience scenic

route therein through life (and immortality, or similar, proportional to square of distance travel). On this excite journey through time, modern 'wristwatch', design to count second, minute and hour, will be of no use. New wristwatch, base on two-dimensional unfold cube model and folding up will feature five attractive face (remaining side is side next to skin on wrist) on which can be counted many (up to 5) dimension of time.

Note: in fourth spatial dimension (soon to be discover) current watch may not work and may indeed appear as like our sundial object or similar. However with six of original wristwatch hypercube can easily be made, as six cubes in third spatial dimension make tesseract which easily will fold into hypercube in fourth dimension, like snow fold into River Warta. Because of strong possibility of fourth dimension and need for modernisation of wristwatch therein, base of each watch is of interlock pin and will fitting together with other wristwatch of equal invention (or to strap, see below). Thereof in said wristwatch.

Claims

1 Object is wristwatch to be worn on wrist in shape of cube, it measure $1\frac{1}{2}'' \times 1\frac{1}{2}'' \times 1\frac{1}{2}''$.

2 Wristwatch cube it fit on metal strap by interlocking pin.

3 Interlocking hinge-pin function with mechanism of finger pressure which fix cube face to strap or to other cube face thereof.

4 Wristwatch measure time in up to 5 temporal dimension.

5 Wristwatch come apart in strap and cube.

6 Cube can fix to other cube. Six of these cube together make tesseract. (Note: tesseract will not fold into hypercube in three-dimensional space.)

7 Watch include time-compass mechanism therein. Time compass not only calculate time in new dimension but provide coordinates if loss of body in time occur (perhaps due to dimension of wormhole, etc).

8 It also include cog-wheel mechanism in three dimensions therein.

9 It have also self-wind mechanism.

Description

Said wristwatch it measure time in up to five temporal dimensions thereof, guarantee to function in three-dimension space only. Watch work by time-compass mechanism (patent pending). Compass is small stainless steel needle suspend in fluid and using magnet to locate and calculate time relative to movement away from or towards y-axis, *not* magnetic North (although principle is similar, although better, as describe in prior application). Compass measure time-direction on depart from familiar line of time, which compass treat like y-axis. On y-axis of knowing time, we are counting by second, minute, hour, etc from Darwin soup and dinosaur through ancient Greeks (Pythagoras, who calculate for right-angle triangle $a^2 + b^2 = c^2$ and Eratosthenes who measure circumference of Earth with stick) to baby Jesus in mange, Roman empire with lion, dark age, middle age, age of steam and so forth to time of splat atom.

But if person on this line wish to take turning right, on x-axis? Law of modern physic say he may not but with wormhole (and even possibility of portable wormhole, patent application in preparation) who know?

Wristwatch keep time as modern timepiece on one face (F_a), tick tock, tick tock, in familial way. However, on leaving y-axis, time-traveller simple go flip with watch cube so internal cog mechanism also go flip and display of time is change. On old face, time stop counting. On 'new' face (F_b) it begin with $y=0$, $x=0$ and count quite simple in second, minute and hour from 0 on x-axis only. Value of $y=0$ is however store on previous face (F_a). If traveller turn left instead of right, new face (still F_b) it count backwards from $y=0$, $x=0$ on x-axis only.

Example: if time traveller turn right from y-axis of time at 6pm on 14th January 1950, he leave behind number 1950a + 14d + 18.00h (Wherein a=year, d=day and h=hour but all expressed on graph of time in seconds from birth of Jesus). If he proceed for one day and two hours along new dimension of time (seeing what sight on way, we ask? Is this to be normal life but in 'parallel world' situation, or other world together? Who know?) then:

$$y = 1950a + 14d + 1800h$$
$$x = 0a + 1d + 2h$$

(where 1h = 60m, and 60m = 3600s)

When convert into second, this easily plot on graph of time. How to convert to seconds? This easily achieve by watch only counting time in seconds and being setted at time of purchase.

So time traveller sit on graph of time slightly to right of previous position on y-axis of 'normality' time. What if he now turn right again? Watch now flip to new face (F_c) which has mechanistic feature that now compute seconds in direction of −y. Think, if traveller proceed for two day and two hours, then turn right again and proceed for one day and two hours, he will emerge on y-axis of 'normality' time day before his time travelling excite it begin! And watch face flip at each turn to give correct time wherever time traveller is in world/s.

Note: time traveller may go right from y-axis and proceed in perpendicular fashion for infinity with no time pass in 'normality' time of y-axis.

Also note: time travel into past ($y = < 0$) may not be permit by law of nature.

Field of invention
Timepiece
Hobby/exploration tool
Time travel
Jewellery

Background of invention
On sunny but chill English winter day, with duck skate on frozen pond I sit eating sandwich and read paper on

park bench. I have appointment with man. At appoint hour I get up from bench and deposit sandwich wrapping inside nearby public bin and feed remain crust to duck. I wait. Man is late. Man is pinhead.

I consider pinhead. He have watch, like me. He know what time to meet. Yet he is not meet. He is late. When he come he say, 'So sorry Mr Czerniak, watch stopped.' What is this 'watch stop'? Watch only stop if pinhead he forget to wind.

For a time after this I consider invention of mechanistic feature which mean watch wind itself. It is this thereof that lead me to invention of self-winding watch mechanism. But whole episode make me think about space and time. Einstein say space and time are as one (also matter and energy as witness in splat atom and result bomb). I wonder how time would be if man (and, indeed woman, or dog) can move through it as duck glide on frozen pond (or even as duck fly in air or submerge in unfrozen pond). While I wait for man (or for Mrs B to make picnic lunch, or any annoy wait) I could do something else at same time, or not *same* time. No. Is not time but similar (although better). Is times.

But how would I know the time? My simple wristwatch would keep ticking, no doubting, but it would keep wrong time. When I return to familial one dimension of y-axis, life-death time, watch would be wrong.

How to fix? With simple said mechanistic device as outline thereof.

RIVERS OF BRITAIN

(*undated*)

I have in my mind to create a story of every river in Britain, there being one river to which I owe my good fortune – if not my wealth! (*Editors' note: Kasimir is surely referring here to the river he threw a grenade into on first arriving in England; see p. 82. The comment regarding his wealth heightens the mystery of his personal fortune.*) This is surely symbolic. I am to a river as Scott is to Antarctic.

So I have begun with a list of those rivers I have visited, added to which I have appended certain memorable image, instance or creature. When this project does finish it will be possible to create a small insignia, like helmet badge, for each river; and this will be one – only one – of many features of my Great River Book.

Possible titles for river book
  Great Rivers of Britain
  Waterways of this Wonderous Nation
  From Beginning to End, So Blue
  Waters of Freedom
  The Wader's Way (or perhaps *The Way of a Wader/One Wader's Way*)

All Downhill (slightly obscure, but because water will
not flow uphill, of course)
Waters Break (perhaps *Waters Break Forth*)
Oh Muddy Bank of Britain
Nation of Fish
To the Ocean – God's Speed!

Certain rivers and characteristic items
Cam – punt
Thames – a mechanical crane
Tyne (Newcastle) – fog
Yare (Norwich) – weaver (Dutch)
Gairn (Scotland) – fox, for Colonel Fox
Dee (Scotland) – (Her Majesty, the Queen – or salmon fly)

ESCAPE FROM ST MARGARET

1 October 1980

Dear Uncle Kasimir,

I hope your move went well and that you're now settled in the Swiss Alps. I really liked your party. Thanks for making time to talk to me because everyone else does their best to avoid me since what happened.

Well, you said if I ever needed any advice I should write to you. I hope that's what you really meant because I think I badly do need some. I know you'll probably say I should talk to Mum and Herman, but I've tried that and they won't listen to me. I wrote them a letter and I didn't even get a reply, so I telephoned them and they said that I am just going through a faze and that I should pull myself together. It was Herman who said that, not Mum. I expect Mum would have written to me if he'd let her. Anyway, I won't go on about that.

Let me tell you what's wrong. You know I was going away to boarding school and that I was worried about it. I know it was my fault – well, some of it was after I got expelled. But it's worse than anything I could have thought of. It's so bad that no one's going to believe how bad, may-be not even you. This is all the truth, though, honestly. I'm writing to you from their now and I am doing it in secret, because they read all our letters home. I'm going to post this in the letterbox next to the church in the village where we go on Sunday. They make us go every week, and twice a week we have to say prayers in the chapel at school first thing in the morning. Once it's in the postbox nobody's going to be able to do anything about it, that's the law. So even if they see me drop it in I will be all right.

First of all I don't have any of my old friends. I knew that was going to happen because this place is so far away from all of them, and they're all still at Cotton Park, anyway. Apart from Mandy who got kicked out too. But she's gone to the other school which is only a bus ride away.

Instead I'm up here in the Lake District in the middle of nowhere. It really is like a prison camp and none of the other girls want to have anything to do with me because they know why I'm here. I don't know how they found out but they did, and it's horrible. I don't know if they're scared of me or if they're just looking down on me. They haven't even said enough so I can find out. But I feel so all on my own.

Next, the sisters who run St Margaret's are un-believable. Really, they are so cruel and heartless. They inspect my hair and my fingernails every morning and if there's anything wrong they slap the back of my legs with a ruler. I have to walk with my back straight, or I have to do detention. And the food is disgusting. But if you don't eat it they put it in a cupboard and make you come back and eat it after school, when it's cold. Honestly, you sit there with it in front of you and can't go until you eat it all. I saw a girl being sick when she ate hers and she didn't come back from the hall until we were all in bed.

Maybe I could cope with this if I was actually learning anything. But it's just like at Cotton Park. All the teachers are thick and they're nuns, so everything has God in it, if you know what I mean. You know my favourite subject's art? Well we aren't even allowed to look at pictures with naked men in them, or at statues like Michelangelo's *David*. All we do is draw fruit. I told the art nun that when I went to Rome with Mum and Dad, before he died, when he was allowed to see the Pope, that there are naked men in all the churches. And she slapped my leg and made me stand with a book on my head the whole lesson. It was impudence, she said.

Please, Uncle Kasimir, what can I do? I'm only fourteen and I can't do this until I leave school. And if I do, I won't know anything when I leave, either. I'll be like all the thickos who I hate.

Love,
Gabi

17 October 1980

My dearest little Gabi,

I am now moved completely to Swiss Alps and, until arrival of letter, was thinking that for once all is well in this world. Your news is, however, terrible to me. My heart is breaking to read of what it is you are going through because I believe that now, in this day of age, such rigorous activity and punishment were thing of past. I certainly believe that boarding school was a place of fun and frolics, although in this I have been sadly misled by literary work of Mallory Tower and similar.

Sometimes hardship and pain are good for mind, body and soul – but only if pain is administer with clever purpose. For example, on many occasion in my youth I lament punishment administered by estimable tutor, Kuss. As time pass, however, the point of my suffering become clear. This is way when suffering at hands of clever person – person who demand respect. Lesson of life must come at cost.

'Kasimir,' he would say to me as I whimper or cry out after punishment, 'one day you will bless me for beating you so,' or he tell me 'Kasimir, hold still your tongue in case you bite it off. Many people feel pain. Some accept and learn from this, others perform own humiliation and cripple selves. Nothing I will do can damage you, only your own fear it will do this.' And one time he tell me: 'When you are man, old man, you will be able to look back over life and see outcome of your own action. You will see what becomes of what you do. As boy, however, you see only beginning. Nothing is yet fulfil and nothing has come to pass which cannot be undone. So, you see, Kasimir, it is for me to prepare you. Look back on life with weak spirit and you will see only what is not there. Look back on life through keen eyes of man with strength, man with spirit who know pain, and you will see truth.' I respect Kuss and so I did trust his way. Because I respect Kuss, I did trust what he do.

This was way also with my father, great military general. He lead many men to death in battle – awful death in pain, alone and slow. Some time he shoot own men in head to stop pain. But did these men run from my father? No. They fear him and they fear death. But these men, they run *with* my father. Every time my father did charge with regiment, expose, at front. He thump chest and dare bullet to enter his heart. He did draw red cross of blood on forehead and scream for Russian sniper to shoot through his brain. Such bravery can only come through clutching fear to bosom and to look beyond these things at goal, at target. To see end over death and destruction is what every man should see.

However, Gabi is young student with artistic temperament, not soldier in preparation for Russian front. I see this distinction, although perhaps nun do not. In truth, next month is crucial. I would like you to examine nun in every detail. You should ask whether pain and discomfort you feel is through weakness in own spirit (unlikely) and inability to search for truth, or if nun are pinhead sadist.

Many good people work in Church, this I know. I am, myself Roman Catholic but many times I do disagree with Church. What I say is this. Among religious community there is from time to time malady. Stupidity and dogma triumph over good sense of Christian message, and so malady.

Can you do this? If you watch carefully and send to me conclusion we will proceed according. Fortunately it is not in nature of institution such as boarding school to check post which arrive, only post which leave. So I am assuming that this letter will remain unopen until you read it.

Please write again to me in one month.

All of my love,
Uncle Kasimir

6 November 1980

Dear Uncle Kasimir,

I know it isn't quite one month yet, but I've got to write to you because of what's happening here. I really can't stand it. I telephoned home and spoke to Mum, but I couldn't say much because Sister Barbara was standing just round the corner from the phone booth listening to me. That's because she saw me post my last letter to you. They didn't give me any tea that day or breakfast the next day because I wouldn't say who I was writing to or what I'd said. I was really clever about it, though, and I eventually said I was entering a competition in a magazine. Sister Margaret made me say prayers in the chapel all afternoon, kneeling down on the hard floor, but after that she didn't say anything else.

Anyway, when I spoke to Mum I couldn't tell her how upset I am. That was mainly because of Sister Barbara, but also because Mum wouldn't let me start talking about anything. She chopped me off the minute I said anything more than tell her what the weather is like. So I couldn't even drop a hint. I would write to them, but I'm scared that they'd show the letter to the nuns, and then I'd be in real trouble.

The only good thing is I think I've made a friend. She's called Sam (short for Samantha) and she got expelled from her school, too. We think its really funny. People who come here are girls whose parents are super rich and couldn't care less about them, or girls like us whose parents aren't rich, but care even less about us. In fact they don't want us around so much they'll pay a fortune they can't afford to have us stuck here, out of trouble. Sam's dad doesn't want her to be here, but her mum and him are divorced and guess what? She's got the stepdad from hell, too, and what he says goes. Sound familiar?

Here's some of the things which have been happening to me and Sam. Honestly, I'm not making a fuss, its all the truth.

Last week Sam got spanked with a slipper on her bottom by one of the nuns. This was really horrible. She had to bend over in front of the whole class so they could see her cry. I couldn't watch but all the other girls did. One or two of them smiled. This was all because Sam got caught with a letter from her boyfriend. You were right, they don't read the post which comes in, but they do search the dormitory when we aren't there. Can you believe they do that? If we have any make-up or jewellery they confiscate it, and give you one slap on the back of the legs for every thing they find. That's the only time I think the other girls get punished at all, and they just get a half-slap. But me and Sam, we're different. If they slap us we get a red mark and bruises which last days.

I got into trouble for making a face at one of the nuns behind her back, Sister Cecilia. She's the person whose meant to teach us music, but all we do is play the recorder (which I can't stand), and sing hymns. It was one of the other girls who told her, too. She pointed at me and put her hand over her mouth as though she was shocked. Anyway, this was unbelievable. Sister Cecilia can't speak English properly – she's French, I think, so she doesn't say much. She only points. She came over and grabbed me by the ear and pulled me up to the black-board. Then she made me hold out my hand and hit me six times with the ruler. It hurt so much but I didn't cry. I held it in all the way through the lesson with the other girls watching me and then afterwards I ran to the toilets in the gym block and cried there.

Sam came and looked out for me, but that made her late for cookery, and so she got detention for a week in the outside hut. The outside hut is a little shed with a desk and a chair on the edge of the netball court. There's just one tiny window which doesn't open with a cross hanging over it and there's no heating. So in the summer it's boiling hot and in the winter it's freezing. They put you in there and they shut the door and lock it until they let you out. There's no toilet, so if you want to go you just have to hold on. I'm sure that's got to be against the law, but nobody's going to listen to us.

What's worst of all, the other girls can come by and peep in through the window while you're in there. They laugh and point. I didn't think people could be so cruel. One of the girls, Laura, whose dad's got a huge mansion in the country, she calls it the dogshed. She says it's like the shed where they keep their hounds and when she saw Sam going in you can imagine what she said.

There are loads of other things. What shall we do? I know what you said in your letter was true, but all this is just really bad, isn't it? You've got to help me, and Sam too.

I nearly forgot, but there's something else, too. When I first got here and Mum and Herman were in the head's office with me there was a knock at the door and the local police sergeant arrived. It was really mad, like I was a criminal or something with all of them saying this and saying that about what I did at Cotton Park and saying they'd all be watching me. Anyway, the sergeant got up and stood right over me, wagging his finger, saying that I should take my medicine without complaining and that I was in good hands with the sisters. I wasn't going to like it, he said, but it was going to do me some good. One day, he said, I'll be thanking them for it. In other words, if you think I should go to the police there's no way I can do that. Mum, Herman, the police – none of them are going to listen to me.

I hope you don't think I'm doing this because I'm stupid or pathetic, and I really am not exaggerating, honestly. I just know that I can trust you, that's all. Sam says to thank you for looking out for us, which is true.

Of course I need to get this posted secretly, first. That's probably going to get me into all sorts of trouble, but it'll be worth it if you can help me. I'm going to take some matches with me when I post it, anyway, and if it looks like someone's going to get it I'll run off and shut myself somewhere and burn it.

Love,
Gabi

12 November 1980

My darling Gabi,

This is truly awful. I will say two things to begin. Number one, I do believe you, in every word. Number two, I will indeed rescue you from this place. I appreciate this situation and of course, in normal circumstance I would go direct to police. However, with past problem at Cotton Park School, uncaring stepfather Herman, and attitude of police sergeant this will not be wise. It cross my mind to contact mother, but I can see that she will not listen either. Always I have been problem to her, excepting when she wish to discuss money matter.

Straight away I must try to lift crush spirit. Regime of humiliation and degrading punishment is for one purpose only, so that you submit in their hands like pet mouse. For experiment or other purpose this is what they wish, for you to be like little mouse, quiet in hole and crawl out only to nibble for food when cage bar does rattle.

To lift spirit I shall tell you inspiring story of my father, great military general. This story he tell me on knee, when I was so young I forget – perhaps only so old that I can remember. It is story of great peril, fortitude and suffering. When my father first tell me this story he did indeed make comparison between himself and mouse – much of my own philosophy, you see, is learn from my father. At this time, as child, mouse appeal to me as suitable image. However, I have now made change to story and do not use mouse but cat as this is more close to lion, as I consider my father. So when I say cat you must picture big cat approaching lion and, at same time, mouse (which is from fidelity to my father adventure).

In youth my father attend military college and every summer in recess it was custom for young officer to go forth as attachment for suitable foreign force. Some officer did go to army in France and some to army in Austria, and so on. My father, he did go to attachment with British Army in South Africa to fight Boers, in Royal Engineers Balloon Section. This was unique experience for his time, although it was possibly some joke to make young Polish cadet spend attachment in balloon division.

Of course, no aeroplane was yet available, and there was no Air Force. Big silver balloons were then used only for inspection, like giant eye to hover and observe enemy position. What shock, would you imagine, to be in trench and assume secrecy only to witness glint in sky of silver balloon. My father was pioneer.

Each balloon was tie by steel cable to cart underneath on ground – in this way balloon was move from place to place like child novelty attach to pram instead of entrusting on wild wind. When time it was to go up in air, chemical did mix and hey presto, up and away balloon go.

At any time balloon contain two men, one in basket and one in dangle ropes who hang above basket, equip with telescope and binocular. When they see something they drop hastily scribble note to ground in heavy envelope which contain brick or similar. Winch man below have to observe closely for this, unless he be hit on head.

Sadly, many did think of balloon as amusing frivolity. If Boer sniper did not shoot hole in balloon, so it quickly sink to ground and shrivel like sad heart, military leader often forget balloon and advance while it still bob like happy spirit in sky.

It was therefore with mix feeling that my father approach paltry task of operating winch. This was least appealing job in Balloon Section. If only, he thought in dreams, he would at least float in air in balloon, watching great battle through binocular. Naturally he did prefer still to be marching in front line of battle – but as I explain in previous letter he undsertand that through patience with pain of mundane, petty task, great thing they would surely follow.

This day was so hot that haze shimmer like water veil above ground. Steel cable for balloon did burn fingers and ox to pull balloon cart lie on side in long grass and complain in loud moo. Air was completely still. Nothing move apart from gnat and unique butterfly.

All of sudden man in balloon shout warning, like distant cry of cormorant who stand alone on tiny island, and drop envelope. It fall with thud direct to balloon cart. This day there was no wind and balloon did fly straight above.

'We come down now,' say note in envelope. 'All is quiet.'

Indeed, it was peaceful afternoon – too hot almost for breath. All division of soldier had advance to other side of nearby forest, leaving balloon attach to balloon cart on forest perimeter. Cart would not pass through tree.

My father slowly winch down men in balloon.

'Hurry up, mate, put back in,' one of men laugh and call, or similar. 'Blimey, what is Polish for get move on?' other cry as he peer down through brassy telescope.

'I know English perfect well,' my father say.

'No more of cheek, sonny,' say elder of two men in balloon with handlepiece moustache. 'Remember I have stripes,' he say, and touch insignia on sleeve. This man was sergeant attach to Balloon Squad because of gammy leg.

'I am sorry, sir,' my father say. He wind down winch with all might, muscles taught, listen as it squeak from strain of cable. Eventually balloon was so low that men inside did step out.

'Right, son,' say sergeant, 'how would you like treat?'

'Sorry, sir?' ask my father.

'It is quiet day,' he say. 'And hot one. I am sending you up in balloon while we perform administrative duty.'

'Yes, sir,' my father did salute.

He step into balloon and sergeant remove brake from winch, allowing balloon to rise. As he rise, my father hear laughter. He look down and see soldier waving as balloon rise higher and high, right until very stretch of cable. Men below were now like toy soldier, but capable of movement. He observe as they erect small canopy and sit at table. On floor of balloon was telescope which he did place to eye and watch as men play cards.

'So this is administrative duty,' he say.

But as he watch he see four other men who creep towards canopy from bush. My father cry out warning, but his comrade they did not hear, so far above them he float. Quickly he take envelope from pouch in basket and look to make note – but no pencil. Instead he place rock in envelope and drop anyway. It fall on cart with small thud to no avail. Gun! my father think; where is gun? But he see balloon have no gun – and as cadet have only small knife. 'Look out!' he cry. 'Look out!' But his voice was like pebble cast into ocean and lost in one moment. In his horror he see creeping men draw knife and attack soldiers, cut throat and slash to stomach so quickly. Both men lie dead.

Who are these attacker? he wonder as heart beat like mechanical stamp. Enemy soldier? Spy? Or thief? He watch through telescope as they search pockets of dead soldier, taking money and cigarette. These men are thief, he think, not soldier. As they search, my father realise one more thing: thief were ignorant of balloon.

But as he think this, from nowhere come gusting wind and balloon lurch, to throw my father against ropes and tear telescope from his hand. Helpless, he see telescope fall away, fall, fall until it hit rock and smash. Even from balloon he hear glass tinkle, like bell announcing holy moment in church, and around him now was similar silence.

Thief did jump alert and look about them. They see cart and one point to winch. Together, all look upwards and wave arm at balloon.

This was terrible moment. For first time my father look about him. Even in time of such peril he find breath remove by sight of mass British Army on other side of verdant forest – he look over all trees and see many thousand infantry in line. My God, he think, what splendid sight! as rifles glint in sunlight, cannon and flag. And beyond British troop across wild veldt grass he did see Boer trench – awesome sight. Boer, he know, was formidable foe. What privilege, even so close to death, to see such majesty.

He look down to ground once more and see thieving men gather round winch. One did start to turn handle and, surely, balloon was beginning descent. What to do? My father was face with dilemma: to reach ground and battle with knife against four thief, or to hurl himself from balloon on to them. If he jump, perhaps at least one would die with him, but if he fight with poor weapon, surely thief would triumph and kill him quickly. So he decide to jump.

Still high, maybe one hundred feet, he climb on to edge of basket, balance with grace of hawk on slendour branch and assess best way to leap. By spread arms and legs like fish, he think, maybe two thief might be maim. He bend knees, and start to count from ten down. Goodbye to all this, he think. Is better to die hero death (attitude to prevail throughout life of great distinction). When he reach five, however, he hear screech noise like owl and balloon go judder to halt. Close enough now to men so he hear, he listen as they curse in cockney accent: 'Blimey, ruddy thing is stuck.'

So! my father think. You are British soldier, no doubt deserter. Curse black soul I shall remedy this.

He continue to count: four, three . . . And then he stop. He listen again.

'Come on, it got to move.'

But balloon did not move. It was stuck – cable jam. Ha, fools! my father think. No doubt extreme heat has warp winch, I am so lucky.

'Traitor,' he call down in sharp militaristic tone. 'All of you dirt.'

'Listen to 'im,' say one thief. 'I think we should settle hash right now.'

'Na, let us have little fun,' say another.

'You know,' he shout up at my father, 'you are stuffing, mate.'

'I would speak too soon,' say my father. 'Perhaps you

desert British Army but it will not leave you to be so easy. You shall receive just desert.'

'Na, mate, you are stuffing. You expect relief patrol soon?'

'Naturally,' say my father.

'Well, we are relief patrol.' They all laugh. 'Only we have relief selves.'

In anger my father cry down to them: 'Relief? Oh, I shall show you relief!' And he urinate from balloon on them. This is disgusting but necessary detail, portraying contempt for which my father did view thief and how shunning fear he embrace danger.

'Dirty bugger, we will have you,' they shout back and renew effort at moving winch. One hit it with metal post so noise ring out – *bing, bing!*

My father did review position. If balloon start to move, so he would jump. If balloon stay stuck, he would deploy second strategy – but what? Always, you see, like cat wandering through city at night he might think of every possible avenue to explore.

At this point matters take serious turn for worse.

'Oi, matey boy,' shout one thief. 'Look what I got.'

My father did look down to see that thief had implement in hand, like wooden cross. He squint but as heat of day bear down on his head and haze encounter all around he could not see detail of what man hold.

'You know what is this?' shout thief.

'What, that baby plaything?' reply my father, wishing not to reveal ignorance of implement.

131

'This is crossbow,' thief say. 'At first I did not wish to waste arrow, but now we will have fun. Ha ha.'

Crossbow. My father was in trap, imprison while floating so free. 'How can this be?' he say. Like sound of sea in desert.

'Beg to us for mercy,' say thief.

'Never!' shout my father. He stand proud overlooking edge of balloon basket and bolt shoot immediately into wicker, straight through, grazing leg. My father did not flinch. These men they want to humiliate him, but he would not show them pain from wound, or show anguish at being target for such deadly sport.

'Oh,' he call to them, 'you miss. Would you like for me to issue instruction, direct you like artillery, left bit, right bit, up down, stop, steady fire? Ha!'

'We was just playing, mate,' say thief.

My father ignore twang of bow and look into basket secretly, searching for implement to use. Bolt pass through bottom of basket and appear from between toe, in army boot.

'You miss,' he shout.

To jump now while they watch him would be of no use. Men would simply step to one side so he hit dust and die ignominious. If he could just find some weapon. But all he see was binocular. Alone, he could do nothing.

In desperation he pick up binocular and hold aloft. 'This,' he say to heaven, 'this is all I have.' My father was religious devout man and it was common for him to request assistance from Lord God. As he raise binocular, sunlight did flash on lens and dazzle him. He close eyes, blink and see star. One more bolt whizz past ear.

Alone, by his self he would surely die, perforate by arrow fire by thief deserter. He could not move, he could do nothing. Only thing to save him must be arrival of help. In this year of 1898 he remember events concerning recent tragedy in Africa of General Gordon of Khartoum who maintain defence for so long until over run just two day before arrival of British relief force. Poor Gordon he lose head – my father did not wish to lose his.

Hoping to clear vision from star he peer on to British Army once more and see little glint all over of army steel beneath Africa sun – and this did spark thought. Light flash on binocular would obtain help. As part of training in army college all cadet did learn survival technique including Morse Code signal with mirror.

Dit-dit-dit dah-dah-dah dit-dit-dit: this was SOS signal. Wasting no time he begin to flash binocular lens toward British Army – from so high he must have appear as if like little star which blink in sky or winking sun. Bolt fly past cheek while imbecile below shout and mock him, but my father know to stick to task – it was only hope. He stand fast.

'Hey, you up there,' shout thief. 'How you fancy to be pin cushion?'

'How you will fancy to be pinhead?' whisper my father.

But he hear noise above him – rip and whistle follow by hiss of gas. Arrow bolt did hit balloon and tear fabric.

Now it was only matter of time before balloon lost all of gas and descend to earth. My father curse. He flash SOS again and again, all this time balloon sinking, noise of thief becoming loud and more clear, more close they become.

'No need for arrows after all,' shout one thief. 'We will do you with bare hands, ha ha.'

My father spirits sink. Almost now he was at level with tree and soon British Army would hide from view so all is lost. But what was this he did see? Flash in midst of British Army lens?

He flash again: Dit-dit-dit dah-dah-dah dit-dit-dit.

And he see flash return! Flash, flash – it was message. He read clear: 'Help on way. Keep up chin.'

With this he smile. He look down; thief were mere twenty feet below all rub hands in glee.

'Greeting to you,' my father did call. 'What entertainment to observe such poor shot. Are you from special platoon for blind? Or simply just pinhead?'

This of course make all thief enraging. They throw curse, stamp feet and shout all manner of obscenity so loud my father feel words like blast from hot oven. This was great pity for them, as being so busy to make oath and noise they did not hear approach of cavalry platoon charging from beneath green and pleasant forest canopy, sabre drawn and so on. Cavalry see at once dead comrades, throat cut and spy band of thief deserter making menace at my father. With little ado they cut all of thief to ribbon for vulture.

So you see, my father was trap in prison which was at first sight not prison. Only to him was truth of situation so clear. From distance balloon must have bob among cloud so pretty, while in truth father was in mortal danger.

This is similar situation to your own. People around you, parents and police do not recognise peril; nun do all in power to break spirit. But like my father, you must keep up chin until cavalry arrive. This will be quickly – I promise with all my heart. Although, as you do know, I cannot make return to England on myself, I have in mind plan to rescue Gabi.

First, however, I must learn more about situation. Tell me description of St Margaret and we will escape her, tell me what is going on at various times, plan of future events perhaps involving general public, routine and so on. You will receive this letter by way of person who call himself Peter. Trust this man and all will be well.

All of my love,
Uncle Kasimir

19 November 1980

Dear Uncle Kasimir,
How brilliant are you! There I was with Sam standing on the edge of the hockey pitch preparing ourselves for another run in the mud when the game gets called off. I

had to stick my hand over my mouth to stop myself cheering. The games teacher was well upset, too. She gave the new groundsman a really dirty look, but he just stared back at her – he looked really scary and old. So we all got told to go and get changed and, as usual, me and Sam are the last ones back in because it means we can sneak out of having a shower, when just as we are going in the door up the sports ramp someone grabbed me by the shoulder. Think how scared I was when I saw the new groundsman. But he just winked at me. 'Hello, love,' he said, 'I'm Peter and I got a little something for you from your Uncle K,' and he gave me your letter. He told us to run along and that once we'd written a reply to put it under the heavy roller, and this is it. Who is Peter and did you get him working here?

Anyway, I've got the answers to everything you wanted to know. Since my last letter (which I got posted without any trouble) me and Sam have really kept our heads down and stayed out of trouble. I know the last thing we need now is for the nuns to be keeping an eye on us all the time. I hope this is what you want.

St Margaret's
St Margaret's is really old and creepy. There's a big wall right the way round it that's about three times taller than me, because it used to be a convent before they made it into a school. It goes all the way round the sport fields and the garden at the front. The actual school building is in the middle of this, it looks like an old town hall, and

our dorms are next to it. They look like cattle sheds because that's what they were before they got converted. You can only get in and out of the walls by one little door at the front or the tradesman's gate round the back way, but that's always locked with a padlock. Anyway, the door at the front is tall and narrow and locked all day and night. If you want to go in or out you have to ring a bell, even if your one of the nuns. Then the sister who's on duty comes and sees who you are and lets you out with the key she has. In other words it's just like a prison camp.

At night the door to the dorm block is locked, and the nurse has a key (although there's a key in a glass-topped box beside it in case of fire). There are ten girls in my dorm, and me and Sam share a bunk bed with me on the top because I feel sick on the bottom.

Timetable
Lessons start at 9 on the dot, but on two mornings we go to chapel, Wednesday and Thursday. We do prep on Saturday mornings and then music lessons in the afternoon until 2. After that we can read or go and walk in the garden, or go into town if a nun comes with us. Needless to say me and Sam never go anywhere, but most of the other girls go every weekend.

Events
There's the Christmas fete on Saturday 13 December and the Carol concert on the 20th, that's all. The fete is a

traditional Christmas thing in the gardens, which all the children from the village down the hill get to come to. The schoolgirls have to look after stalls and things like that. At least they let us choose which one to do, and the other girls are so lazy they won't exactly be running to help out. So I suppose I can do what I want. Afterwards we have to help pack everything away. There are rides, too, and a Santa Grotto which the priest dresses up and sits in.

I'm going to stick this under the roller after lunch. I suppose we'll have to wait for Peter to tell us what to do? Don't worry, now we know you're helping us its much more easy to keep our spirits up.

I love you so much, Uncle Kasimir (and Sam sends a kiss for you as well, she thinks you are really brilliant).

Lots of love,
Gabi

24 November

My dearest Gabi,

I am so pleased to hear you sound happy. Peter is very useful fellow, is he not? I meet him in Borough Market, London Bridge, shortly after war, where he did sell knock off lemon and similar. Later I employ him in all manner of job. Sometimes he did get into scrape, for example obtain petrol for truck and forget to pay, but in general he is honest sort, cockney, straight as die and man of great resource. I believe that competition for job of groundsman was to begin with intense, until all other applicant did withdraw application. What stroke of luck for us!

I am reading description of school which you provide. Security is indeed formidable, no doubt because of initial role as haven for nun. However, as I have said before, school institution is more keen to examine what go out – pupil, good grade, and so on – than what come in. With this in mind I have spoken with Peter regarding Christmas fete and this is what you must do.

It is imperative that you work on 'Mr Bubbles' stall and do precisely what Peter say. All else will follow with ease.

One further thing does of course remain. You will appreciate that getting you out of school is simple task, but not end of problem. Where then will you go? I do not doubt for one moment that Bavarian stepping father will have you pack back on next train to St Margaret. Please do not let this concern you as all will be deal on this score as well.

Good luck!

All of my love,
Uncle Kasimir

16 December 1980

Dear Uncle Kasimir,

I can't believe you! That was probably the most funny and exciting thing which has ever happened to me, and to Sam as well.

I thought it was a bit weird when I got to the Mr Bubble stall and found that Peter had already set it up with hundreds of balloons tied around the banner saying its name, 'MR BUBBLE' – there really were hundreds. He must have been doing it for ages. I thought we were trying to keep a low profile, not stand out as the most colourful stall at the fete. Then, when Sister Barbara came past and she took one look at it all and said we'd be in it right up to our necks if one single balloon blew away and caused a nuisance, I thought we'd really done it.

'What exactly is Mr Bubble for?' she asked us.

'Balloons,' said Peter before we could say anything. 'Little balloons for the tots.' And he pointed at a box of smaller balloons than the ones he was tying up the banner. 'Not these ones what I'm tying, of course. Soon as I finish off these big ones the girls are gonna blow up them little ones, tie on a bit of ribbon, and Bob's your uncle.'

'Can't you just use the ones you've tied round that banner?' She made a face. 'There are so many of them.' The balloons were all bobbled together in three big clumps, like the round bits of giant raspberries, going up way into the air.

'Nah,' said Peter. 'Got to think of safety. If one of those kiddies pops one of those big balloons next to its ear and perforates an ear drum you won't hear the end of it. And nor will they.' He laughed. 'They want little ones.'

Sister Barbara didn't laugh. She sort of scowled and shook her head. 'Just one balloon creating a spectacle,' she said to me, wagging her finger. 'Just one . . .'

Peter winked at me and kept on blowing up balloons from his big cylinder and tying them to the banner. Then he told us he had got to 'Love us and leave us', but to pull the string when we heard him toot his car horn. 'What string?' I asked. And he gave me a long string dangling out of all the balloons. Then he wandered off whistling. What car horn? I thought, the minute I couldn't see him any more. Sam couldn't think what he meant either.

We just stood there letting all the kids have little balloons which we filled off the cylinder, put a knot in and fastened some ribbon to.

I think it was about half past three when I heard a car engine.

'What's that?' I asked Sam.

She looked around while I kept filling the little balloons, but she couldn't see anything. Then I heard a car horn. There were three long blasts. Wherever it was it wasn't far away.

'Pull the string,' said Sam.

I yanked it really hard and it came away, like it wasn't properly tied to anything. I kept pulling, and suddenly all the balloons, every single one of them, flew off into the air. Well, they didn't really fly much, they just kind of dropped on to the ground, blew about and bounced, hundreds of them. It was like they didn't have quite enough gas in them. I looked at Sam and she looked at me, and we wondered if something had gone wrong. The whole fair was swamped by loads of bouncing balloons.

They caused chaos. It was so funny. All the people were tripping over them. Some of the nuns and the other girls started running about trying to catch them and pop them, but that just made it worse. I could hear Sister Barbara shouting our names, but she was hidden somewhere by the balloons. All the wind they made rushing about stirred up the balloons like Smarties in a cake recipe, trapped by the high walls all round the garden.

All of a sudden we saw Peter waving to us from near the medical tent.

'Get a move on!' he shouted, 'Look lively.'

We ran for it. When we got to the tent we saw he had his car – a Porsche – parked behind it, and we all jumped in. Sam had to sit on my lap. He reversed at about a hundred miles an hour, right out of the tradesman's entrance (which was wide open, I suppose they let the groundsman have a key), and off we went with him singing that song about lions, 'Born Free'.

By the time Peter dropped me off at my house (we took Sam home first) the police were there and Mum and Herman were so angry! Anyway, it's a good thing Peter did a disappearing act because I think they wanted to do him for kidnapping. I didn't say anything to the police at all and they told Herman that no one had actually committed an offence and it was all a waste of their time. So they went off leaving him and Mum fuming.

Of course the school were straight on the phone telling me not to come back, and Herman was already looking for somewhere else to send me – only that's when you rang up by chance (what a coincidence!) and told them not to worry, that you knew of a school that would sort me out, and that you'd pay for it, too – it was the least you could do. No wonder Herman got so excited. They packed me off on Monday morning and here I am.

I was a bit worried to begin with. I mean this is the third school I've been to this year and it's got a bit of a weird name. Only when I saw that all the girls were allowed to wear what they want, I was so happy. Apparently P—— is what you call a 'progressive' school, only you know that already, don't you? Finally, and I can't ever thank you enough for this, when Sam arrived the next day and said you'd sorted it for her to keep me company, I nearly cried.

I love you I love you I love you. You're the best uncle in the world, ever, EVER, and I really mean that.

I love you always and always and for ever,
Gabi
XXX

COMMON MISTAKES IN ENGLISH: TERM OF SCIENCE

(October 1946)

Recent mistake and correction therein. Must learn, Kasi. As man of science, now study for Diploma in Chemical Engineering at prestigious University College London, must make not error in such way. In common room talk is of space, extend world of great men of science (like Gamow and Hoyle). Must improve English.

Relativity and Relative

Einstein he not make theory of relative. A relative is person from family, like mother or brother or similar. Relativity, invent by Einstein, great European genius, say however fast you go, light it move faster, at same rate, c, for ever. Some would say mother also do this. But she relative, still, to what who can know?

Newton and Neutron

Newton see apple fall to earth and invent gravy. He does not living inside nucleus of atom. This is neutron. Practise for 'r' sounding.

Satellite and Set Alight

'Rachel she satellite heart of Caruthers.' Wrong and Embarrass. Satellite is Earth to sun, object orbit in space. Set Alight is to make fire of object. Rachel from nurse college love Caruthers, red-cheek English man, not Kasi, 'halfwit Pole'.

Mole and Mould

This extreme confuse. Penicillin is not discover when Fleming he find Mole on plate. He find Mould. In similar, Mould it not live in garden of Mrs B house. This is Mole, he annoy. But most confuse: Mole not only annoy animal in hole but also measure of substance in chemist.

Clock and Cock

In relativity universe, Cock move slow if spaceman move fast. This is right but for simple matter that Cock it crow in morning and Clock go tick tick on wall (or in relativistic spaceship). This cause erupt of laugh from C and P. Why?

Vector and Victor

Victor live on ground floor of Mrs B house. Vector it measure size and direction at same time. Victor, although nice chap, he does not doing this. 'Vector, I see you have another package from postman today.' No.

Ferrous and Fairies

'It is Fairies metal.' Is Kasi cuckoo in head? Ferrous it mean like iron. Fairies, magical creature, do not exist in world of science (although mother still maintain they in vegetable garden).

Salt and Assault
Salt is result of react of acid and alkali. Assault is when one man hit another (perhaps in smug red cheek). 'Do you mean to salt me?' No, sir, I will Assault you.

Analysis and Anastazia
Not very similar word but everything it make me think of my Ana and so I make mistake. How she? Rachel not love Kasi. Ana love Kasi. Kasi love Ana. This is simple. But mother preference Rachel girl for Kasi (girl of good parent) and not my Ana. Mother say my Ana 'no good'.

Electron and Election
Churchill, great war leader, did not defeat in general Electron. This is Election. Particle which orbit nucleus of atom is called Electron. Also learn word Erection which mean building and also is not name of element particle or system of vote. 'In Britain, democratic island, the people hold general erection.' I have only tell this to mother and she not understand English but must not say again.

Rocket and Rock
One day man will perhaps fly in Rock to space. No. Another embarrass moment in common room. Caruthers again say, 'Kasi is halfwit' and Parker nod head in agree.

Pump and Pimp
Kasi Pump fluid, bicycle tyre, &c. I Pimp this tyre for you
madam. This mean nothing. I will Pump your tyre: yes.
Who was fair maiden on stormy highway name of
Holloway Road? I probability never know. It not my
Ana.

Friction and Fiction
Friction it is force which hinder motion of two
surface. Fiction it book, or lie. *The Machine of Time*
is great work of Friction': no. 'I skid not on path due
to Fiction': also wrong. Must keep practise for 'r'
sounding.

Fission and Fishing
Fission is where giddy nucleus it split as in chain reaction
or A-bomb. I do not go Fission with Mr B. With him I go
instead Fishing. To catch Fish, slime swim in water and
eat with chip. Fishing do not take place in atom.

Planet and Plant
Planet ball in sky, orbit sun. Planet not grow in window
box. 'That is healthy Planet, Mrs B': no!

Particle and Particular
I have Particle problem I have to say with you Mrs B. It
concern my use of Particular accelerator in bedroom.
No! Particle accelerator.

Red Shift/Blue Shift and Unmention Word
This so embarrass on Monday I do not know if can show face again in common room with smug face of Parker, Caruthers and Dupont. 'Shit' is word shout by British soldier on explode shell, shot whiz past ear or similar. It bad word similar although not better, to Polish word Kurwa (although meaning is not same). 'Today we hear of Red Shit coming from distant star.' No, no, *No!*

NARRATIVE FOR CHILDREN

Chapter One

'It is Easter hols once more!' cry Stefan, running through dusty school hallway. 'Hoorah, by Jimmy!'

'Just as I was thinking hols would never arrive,' say Marek, blond boy, good at sport, lithe like shorn sheeps.

'Let us pack and depart immediately,' Stefan say. 'Anastazia, Helga and Regina will already be at home, and will be waiting to hear our plans. And, of course, Mayfair the rabbit, found some three years ago at Mayfair in London. We must plan for meeting of Superior Six as soon as is convenient to us all.'

'Rather!' Stefan say, and ran off to dormitory to pack school trunk.

'Goodo,' said Marek, but Stefan have disappeared in puff of smoke.

The next day both boys were picked up by father of Marek. Stefan was unfortunate, ill fate orphan and so spent every holiday with family of Marek.

'Aye, boys,' say father of Marek, imposing man with beard like wild white sponge, monocle and wooden leg which tap like pecker-bird, from period of sea-captaincy and bounty.

'Father, why not tell us a seafaring story on way

home!' exclaim Marek, clambering in back of car, a young chimp.

But father was distant as if in dream, perhaps from shell (for he had also been Naval Captain in War against Hitler) and so did not do as son requested.

'No, Marek,' he say instead. 'There will be plenty of time for stories when we get home.' He pull off in car, four tyres crunching on school driveway like hoof of mule upon bitter Polish snow.

Marek settle down instead to talk to friend, poor orphan Stefan (who wheeze, through birthright of asthma and contagion).

Then his father interrupt. 'Actually, boys, there may be more time for stories than you think, when we get home to family house in roll countryside.'

'Why, father?' ask Marek.

'There is dangerous criminal hiding out in woods,' he say. 'So Superior Six will not be having adventures this Easter, I can tell you this for nothing. No, there will not be adventure this hols.'

'No adventure?' say Marek, sad as fish with hook in head.

'No adventure?' repeat Stefan, quieter than Marek due to orphan lung.

'No,' say Marek father. 'You will instead be reading Bible and considering Easter message of Christ bleeding on cross, with crown of thorns, He who live and die and rise again for us. This is what good children do at Easter.'

Marek look even sadder. Perhaps fish with no head at all, beaten on riverbank.

'How do you know that dangerous criminal is hiding in woods?' ask Stefan.

'We see smoke from fire,' Marek father say.

'Have police not therefore snatched him from hiding hole?' ask Marek.

'No,' say Marek father. 'When they go to woods he give them a slip.'

How peculiar, but not a shock to the children of course. Rarely did police collar criminal. Most of time it was left to children to do job for them.

'What is dangerous about criminal, father?' ask Marek.

'He eat babies,' say father.

'He eat babies?' say Marek. 'Golly gosh.'

'All apart from ears, which are found in woods. Sometimes ears are not found for several days and are therefore rot.'

'How thrilling!' say Stefan to Marek under breath. 'We must call meeting of Superior Six at once.'

'On double,' agree Marek in whisper. 'We will apprehend foul criminal!'

Chapter Two

When car pull into driveway of exclusive mansion belonging to family of Marek, the girls, Anastazia, Helga and Regina, were already waiting. Mayfair the rabbit was still in hutch. In excitement, girls had forgotten to release him.

Anastazia hated full name and instead was always called Ana. She was tall like tree, with blonde hair in two long plaits like frond of weeping willow. She was twin of Marek and his senior by ten and a half minutes – fact which she never let him forget!

Regina was youngest child of family. She hate getting dirty or muddy and going in water. She was more of girl than Ana or Helga. Helga was cousin of all but orphan Stefan. Helga was Tomboy, which mean she like to climb tree.

When boys get out of car, domestic servant come to take away trunks.

'Have you heard?' Ana say to the boys.

'Yes,' say Marek, nodding like grave. 'There is baby-eater on loose in forest.'

'We must call meeting,' she say.

'Yes, of course, but you are girl, even if eldest, so I will call meeting at my convenience,' say Marek.

'Well do hurry up,' say Ana. 'Everyone else are ready. Mother has even provided us with topping cake left over from yesterday supper, and Helga is fetching some lemonade.'

Just then Helga appear, carrying tray laden with scone, lard, bread and egg. She look like blossom in spring, but dressing as cowboy.

'Hallo Marek, hallo Stefan,' she say.

'What is this?' Stefan ask.

'This is rations of domestic servants,' she say. 'Mother said we could have them for secret meeting. She say they will not starve in one day. Oh do say there will be a meeting, Marek, or we will have to feed it all to Mayfair!'

Marek clear his throat and say like solemn burgher: 'I hereby call official meeting of Superior Six, beginning now in secret hideout. Do not be late.'

With that, he walk off toward back of house and was gone.

'Secret hideout?' say Helga.

'Ah, Marek has not told you,' say Stefan.

'He told me in his recent letter to boarding school,' say Ana. 'Come on everybody, I will lead you there.'

'It not in forest, is it?' say Regina, shivering in blouse.

'Of course not, silly,' say Ana. 'Come on everybody!'

CHURCH BELLS

14 April 1968
On hearing church bell from afar

These things of wonder – is it surprise that, today,
church bells still peal across our British nation?
Vivos voco, mortuos plango (I call the living, I mourn
the dead) – inscription from a church bell
Campanology = study of Bells
Fen ling: wind bell with clapper and metal plate.
Big Ben: famous London bell. Largest of five
bells.
Change ringing. In Britain bells can be peeled
so: bells are rung in different mathematical per-
mutations.
Quasimodo – of Notre Dame (Paris)

(lighthearted)

> Oh bell, oh bell
> Oh well, oh well
> When you ring
> I do sing
> So well, so well.

CHURCH BELLS

(to rhyme orange!)

A bell will peel
Quicker than an orange
On one cold eve
As I suck a lozenge

ON BEING MAN

My dearest Kasimir,

I hope that all is well with you. Time flies so very quickly, don't you think? It seems like yesterday that the three of us, you, Herman and I, were sitting on your balcony admiring the views of those wonderful snow-capped mountains. Believe me, when you raised that last glass of your finest port and toasted our safe journey home, I never thought so many years would pass without me seeing you again.

Such is life. I recall the excellent meals you cooked for us, accompanied by some splendid wines. Herman remains sure that he's never drunk better wines than the ones from your cellar. Then there were all those bracing walks in the crisp mountain air. Do you remember how you held our little Oscar's hand and pointed out the different kinds of birds to him along the way – how old was he then? Just turned seven? You left such a great impression on him. Even now, whenever he sees something unusual flapping its wings in the sky he turns to me and says: 'You know, Mummy, I bet Uncle Kasimir would be able to tell us what that one's called.' I expect you would, too.

Would you believe that Oscar turns eighteen next month? The boy becomes a man! Of course Herman is thrilled – at long last he'll be able to take his son up to his clubs with him. Goodness knows, I can see them getting up to some mischief together. I think they're planning to take a boys' shooting trip to the Highlands later in the summer. Not, of course, that we will be able to afford such extravagances soon, with Herman's retirement coming up, and with the continual pressures from his ex-wife, but life goes on.

I wondered if there's any way that you'd like to mark Oscar's eighteenth? He'd be so excited to hear from you and, these days, it makes so much sense for families to bond around these occasions. It's a very important but stressful time for a young man, with so many choices to make, to say nothing of the financial obligations that go with university and setting yourself up in life. I'm sure a man of your great experience doesn't need any further telling what I mean. A gift from you would mean so much to Oscar and would relieve some of the pressure on Herman at this difficult time. After all you have done for Gabi, it would be only fair.

I hope that you are keeping well and that soon we may be reunited. Who knows, perhaps next year we may be able to find our way to Switzerland? I hear they are doing some very reasonable deals now.

With love,
Your niece, Anna

1 May 1995

Dear Anna,

I am glad that events so distant remain fresh in your mind. Similarly I am pleased that the Bavarian retains fond memories of my cellar, modelled of course on family cellar looted by Germans during the war. Perhaps it is my destiny to satisfy Teutonic palate.

I am delighted to hear that my great-nephew will soon celebrate eighteenth birthday. It comes as great relief to hear how great an impression I did make on him – having heard nothing in last ten years I had assumed that he had forgotten uncle in Swiss Alps. But it is no matter. I wish Oscar only the very best in the world and have, after much thought, enclosed for him my gift.

Naturally you will be most welcome should you decide to visit me. Perhaps Oscar could come to Swiss Alps with you instead of to Scottish Highlands for shooting with Bavarian. This is of course not for me to say.

With great love,
Your uncle, Kasimir

1 May 1995

My dearest Oscar,

Very soon you will be eighteen. As is custom in United Kingdom, reaching such an age opens wide a gateway into adulthood. In eyes of law, you will be a man. However, the measure of a man is not in years, but in his heart. Not in his face, with newly grown beard or moustache, but in his mind. This I know you will find hard to appreciate. Many will expect you to behave like man while still treating you like boy, or they will treat you as man without realising you have still mind and heart of boy. At times this will always be so, however old you are. In all men is heart and spirit of boy. After many years all men understand this.

To become true man is now more difficult than at any time. Today, what is man? In my youth, to become man was more straightforward matter – solemn family affair conducted in private, doubtless very different from raucous celebration you envisage for your eighteenth birthday. Indeed my own eighteenth birthday was inconsequential affair – celebration of manhood occurred years earlier (although real discovery of true manhood it takes many more years, as you will grow to understand).

As I have already said, I have no drunken party. On morning of twelfth birthday I was woken in hours of darkness by Blazej Kuss, estimable tutor.

'Kasimir,' he ask me, 'what day is this?'

'It is my birthday,' I tell him. Then I smile a little, as previous birthdays had been occasions of great joy throughout household, with father, great military general, playing accordion. Kuss see smile and take hold of my ear.

'Kasimir,' he say, his voice like whisper of Siberian wind, 'this is not day for levity. Get dress.'

I jump from bed and dress quickly in simple clothes to match mood of solemnity. While I did this, Kuss did stare from window on to grey mists of first light. 'You know what you must do,' he say quietly.

'Yes sir,' I reply in sombre voice. I know. I remember instruction.

Together we proceed to library. Already my father, great military general, was sitting behind desk stroking moustache.

'So, my son,' he say, placing hands on heavy military sword lying across desk. 'Do not disappoint me.'

I tremble as I approach him, eyes of Kuss on my back like claws of cunning animal, perhaps bat. As I arrive at desk my father slide heavy steel sword towards me. I did stand on tiptoe and grip cold metal handle. Slowly, and with difficulty, I raise great sword above my head until tip was close to chandelier. Then I step back from desk five paces and lower sword until it point directly at my father's throat, straight above desk. My arms feel like they might break, but I did not drop sword. Luckily, my father immediately took hold of sword tip and I stare along flat of blade directly into his eyes.

Previous day in arithmetic lesson Kuss told me how I was to lift sword on father's desk in preparation for test of manhood. Why I was to lift sword did remain unknown to me and I tremble then, wondering what this task would be.

'Kuss,' my father say, 'boy is ready.' Great military general did not smile, he did not grimace. Like dark waters of River Warta, princess of Polish rivers, expression reveal to me nothing.

Kuss answer: 'Very good.' He step outside door and speak briefly to waiting servant. I hear rustling of straw in box and, to my great surprise, sound of puppy barking. Kuss he say one word and dog was falling silent. He return carrying puppy in arms – beautiful little black dog with neck wrapped in white fur collar.

'My gift to you,' say my father. 'If you are man enough to keep her.'

Kuss place dog so it is sitting beneath flat blade of sword. With free hand my father wrap great fingers around dog body, holding creature in place like glue.

He then turn blade until sharp edge was rising above little puppy head, as executioner axe – was I to be executioner? My heart it did pump and my knees did shake as foundations of timber hut in flood. If my father had not been supporting tip of sword, weapon would have already fallen and cut animal in two, like apple. Puppy look up at razor-sharp edge and then towards me, trusting expression of hope in eyes. Although this perhaps I imagine.

From shelf behind my father Kuss took hour glass, ancient object long kept in family. He put it on desk beside puppy and addressed me most seriously.

'Kasimir, I will turn the hour glass and your father

will release tip of blade. If after one minute, when sands run empty, you have not let sword fall, your father will release this puppy. However, if you should let sword fall, then dog will surely die, slice desparate in two. If dog lives she will be your companion in manhood. If she dies, you will weep over corpse as a child.'

With this Kuss reach out and turn hour glass. At exact same moment my father let go of sword tip and immediately blade was falling. I cry out and brace myself, leaning back hard, employing all my strength. I curse like a man and cry out my name as warrior in battle: '*Kas-i-mir!*' It was enough – falling of sword was in termination one inch above puppy head. In curiosity puppy lift nose and sniff cruel blade in ignorance of my straining muscles and failing spirit. 'No!' I shout, watching blade slowly start to dip. 'No!' I cry again as sword start to vibrate with my shaking arms, weight of all that I knew upon them. Tears did fill my eyes. Hour glass was only half empty.

'Kasimir!' shout my father, voice of great military general sending shock through my spine, locking my arms in terror. 'Allow dog to die and you are not fit to be my son. Man must protect those who are weaker than he.' His face was now red, grip upon puppy like iron talon so it have bulging eyes. Puppy quiver at might of great military general. 'A man must find strength where others cannot. Let sword drop and I will send you from this house to live with creatures in field, such will be your shame.'

I gaze at hour glass, my head beginning to spin as if in storm. It is quarter full.

'Kasimir,' whisper Kuss, sound of his voice like water on hot coals, 'you will not drop sword. If you drop sword I will punish you in such a manner you cannot imagine.'

At this I find strength firing my bones and muscles. As runner in sight of finishing line I let out roar and lift sword. Puppy whine from grip of great military general and roar of his young tiger. I continue to lift sword.

'Ha!' I cry.

'My son!' exclaim my father, eyes damp from tear, broad smile replacing grim anticipation of defeat.

Kuss say nothing. He point to hour glass. Sands all gone.

My father release puppy and usher it from beneath sword. It tumble in heap against work of Tolstoy – and I bring sword down fast, like man. I split desk in two. My father cheer – such a sound I have never before or since heard. Roar of furnace, noise of sun in explosion. He kick desk out of way and tread over broken wood and torn papers to embrace me. Lifting me in air he clasp me against chest, familiar scent of gun metal filling nostrils. 'My son,' he shout in ear, 'you are *man*.'

Kuss did click heels together and bow head at me. In nebulous expression perhaps I detect joy, perhaps regret. Always I have wonder what was his promise punishment and whether this or my success were foremost in his mind.

This was my father gift to me: act to test fortitude in

163

mind and body. Now, in later years of life, I can see how many things this act prepared me for. But for you, each challenge you meet will be your first and for real. No rehearsing. Would my father have allowed sword to fall? But of course. Would he have let dog die? No, swiftly he would move dog to safety. My father was true man.

And this tale is my first gift to you. Reflect upon it often as it has much to teach you. Of course, little dog was Anna Karenina, first Anna Karenina, who live long and happy life as my companion, dying peacefully on eve of war.

As my second gift to you I offer my observations on such things which may confuse or trouble you in years ahead. These I have drawn from my own experiences in hope that you will make better use of life than

(Editors' note: the remaining pages are missing.)

A TELEVISION SERIES

1 August 1969

Mr Patrick Moore
The Sky at Night
C/o BBC Television Centre
Wood Lane
London

Dear Mr Moore,

I did watch with great interest your report of historical Apollo XI Moon Landing on moon. Did I ever think to see day when man would walk on moon, nearest (and only) satellite of our own Earth? No, I did not. But what next, does one ask? Perhaps the Red planet Mars? I am in agreement with astronaut Armstrong when he says it is one giant leap for mankind to land on moon – but like Olympic athlete, the hurdle of Mars will surely not long evade our mighty jumping men either.

However, I write to you in some hope of your advice. I am millionaire, but in many ways still unhappy with my moral coil. In recent times, spur on by kind support of my good friend and neighbour Mrs Marjorie Petigrew, former Headmistress, I have made attempt to pursue vocation of an artist. With regret these have fallen on to stony ground and, with heavy heart, I have been ready to perhaps face the reality that my ambitions would be for ever defeated. (I have enclosed for your pleasure copies of my greatest works: 'The Robot Foot' and 'Once Upon Some Storm Struck Night', a poem – of which I have also written many.)

Your recent broadcast has however renew hope of me realising my dreams. You will notice certain robotic references within 'The Robot Foot' and to these I would add my enjoyment for last year's cinematic spectacle, *2001: a Space Odyssey*, together with the BBC's own *Dr Who* (in particular 'Power of Daleks'), and not least your own informative guide to mysteries of Outer Space, *The Sky at Night*. Given all things considered (Arthur C. Clarke; 1960 first heart pace-maker implanted; 1963 first cassette tape machine; 1964 home kidney dialysis; 1967 breathalyser first used on car drivers; 1968 Russian T-144 is first supersonic airliner; etc) perhaps time is ripe for my own scientific television series.

If you would be so kind, as man of great scientific bearing, knowledge of outer space and successful television presenter, I wondered if you would examine proposal contained here within for television series *Blast Off!*

In hope of your comments I have included 'synopsis' of episode one (as I understand is usual practice), full working of some scenes, certain notes on main characters and also several sketches (with annotation) of robotic machines I believe would grip the viewer.

I would be most grateful of any advice you have to offer, persons to whom I might submit my work, and so on. Do you, perhaps, know Stanley Kubrick, actor Captain Kirk or Patrick Troughton? If so perhaps you would be so kind to submit my work to them directly. If this is the case please tell me if you require assistance with necessary postage.

Yours sincerely,
Kasimir Czerniak

BLAST OFF!

Overview
In tradition of many great works of science fiction it is my intention to grow seedling of *Blast Off!* with 20th-century jet engineering, for instance; or to harness consummate power of contemporary Timelord of *Dr Who* with arresting spirit of bloodthirsty ghoul Vlad Impaler (Transylvanian Monarch), I hope to achieve work of timeless fiction.

Synopsis
Enigmatic Timelord Professor Kuss (is he good or is he bad?) is engaging in titanic struggle with Elves which is shaking cosmos. With young assistant, Kipper, talking

(and often singing) dog from distant planet (in all respect Kipper is as human boy, eating, speaking, breathing as young man – but is in fact dog. Kipper will sit on a chair to eat meal using special cutlery adapted for paws; and he will walk also on hind legs, as I have seen dog trained for Russian circus), it is up to Professor Kuss to avert end of civilisation. Elves have discover secret of jet flight and can drop from Mars to Earth, then to return (with jets) laden with all bounty of humanity. Can Professor Kuss and Kipper (also Anja, see below) stop this theft before Elves have steal all that is dear to humanoid? Or will Elves outwit majestic Timelord and his dog (who is almost as boy)? And what of estimable Professor Kuss ('Is he good or is he bad?' – I suggest this as suitable catchline for posters, etc)? Viewers will be left to wonder whether world will in fact be better place with Professor Kuss instead of Elves.

Cast Notes

Professor Kuss, Enigmatic Timelord

Is he good or is he bad? I know of very man to play this part, sadly vanished in wake of Allied treachery as Poland thrust into jaws of Stalin (1945, Yalta). Still, dedicated method actor will no doubt be able to live part to sufficiently. I would suggest actors Robert Redford and Paul Newman for such role although both would need coaching in accent of England (possibly 'Cockney' accent?). As alternate, Peter Sellers would make good Kuss.

Kipper
'The dog with the heart of boy' (again, I would suggest this line as suitable to use on posters and other advertisements). Kipper, as explain elsewhere, does come from distant secret planet where dogs are like people and people are similar like pets. Kipper's planet has name, but one which no human can pronounce (hence I give it no name). In series, references might be making to 'Planet Kipper', planet of singing dogs. It is hoped that later in series leader of Planet Kipper may be revealed and I would pray Mr Dick Van Dyke would make available himself for the playing of this part.

Anja
A 'pet' from planet of Kipper. Anja has soul of a kitten but appearance of young girl. Unlike kitten she will not walk on four legs and lick from bowl of milk – to me, audience would find this disturbing. Instead Anja will purr and enjoy to be stroked. Anja has 'supersense' (a term I have invent for this series) and can overhear distant conversations in garden, opening of doors, rat, etc, like real cat. Vanessa Redgrave will be terrific audition in this part.

Super Elf
The Elf king – ugly two-and-half-foot-tall thief and tyrant. I arrive at this measurement of Super Elf from surveying the Elf Hole, mythical elvish grotto in Cornwall with small entrance. Midget will be need to be

found to play this part. Possibly from circus or cast of *Wizard of Oz*. Or else Harry Secombe film through particular lens.

Many other characters appear in this series.

Sample Script

Episode 1, Scene 1

Whitstable, a Sunday afternoon

It is 1935, and there is respectful Bobby and air of tranquillity in all that is English in pre-war nirvana: red pillar box, cricket match (for it is Sunday) being played on village green and vicar lifting hat to passer by. Distant dog yaps and overhead buzzes ancient biplane (to make contrast with imminent appearance of rocket-Elf). Young lady in long skirt talks to young man dismounting from bicycle within shrubbery close to cricket match.

ELSIE, YOUNG WOMAN (*She is plain to avoid sympathy of audience reaction. Elsie is minor character, unlike Anja who is very pretty girl-cat*): Don't you be so cheeky, Alfie.

ALFIE, YOUNG MAN: Crikey, Elsie, you are having laugh. Elves?

ELSIE: I seen it with own eyes, Alfie, so don't you be calling me liar.

ALFIE: Ha! Ha! Next you'll be telling me you have gone and seen man in moon! Goodness gracious. (*He rest bicycle against wooden post.*)

ELSIE: Look out, Alfie! (*She point behind him, look of terrible fear tormenting face.*)

170

ALFIE (turning slowly): Now what have you gone and . . . Heavens beyond!

Elsie scream. We do not see what Elsie and Alfie have seen, but cut instead to cricket player who is out due to ball hitting stump. He curses luck and gesture towards continuing scream in shrubbery.

CRICKETER 1: I say, what in Dickens is happening?

MAN IN WHITE COAT (umpire): You are bowled out as ball has hit stump. You must leave pitch.

CRICKETER 2 *(who watches from outer field)*: Play up and play game, sirrah.

There is sudden awful rushing sound – a jet motor like one never heard before (no doubt, as jet engine was not invented). Cricketer 1 is grabbed from force above and lifted into heavens with yell. All other players look upwards.

CRICKETER 2: God in heaven. That has torn it.

MAN IN WHITE COAT: Blimey, that was elf. Am I hallucinate?

At this moment Elsie runs from shrubbery, clothing tattered and like rag. She is screaming. Several cricketers run to give aid.

CRICKETER WITH THICK BEARD: It is all right, love. Do not worry.

ELSIE: The elves! The Elves. They have taken Alfie.

Look of horror on all cricketers' face. Vicar collapse by gate.

CUT TO:

Episode 1, Scene 2

Another dimension, time immaterial

Timelord Professor Kuss (is he good or is he bad?) stands astride control lever of Mighty Ark, space and time machine (see notes on machines at end). This lever it is like giant pole emerging from floor and is to navigate space and time. He wears cape to ankles and stirring uniform of hero.

Enter Kipper, walking on hind legs. Kipper wears 'plus four' trousers in manner of Edwardian gentleman (for Kipper is fop), golfing shoes and velvet smoking jacket. He is sporting 'pince-nez' spectacles to enhance air of intellectual (this is most important as heart of man within body of dog must shine forth, in radiation of wisdom). In manner of leader of Planet Kipper, he will sing all lines (in similar style of Mary Poppins *or* Chitty Chitty Bang Bang *as this is series for young and old and both young and old may feel fright at elves).*

KIPPER (singing and dancing): Professor Kuss, I am receiving signal from the planet Earth.

PROFESSOR KUSS: !!!!

Anja falls from upper cabin locker where she nap but land on four legs, like cat (although clearly as mention earlier I wish to play down cat behaviour). She purr.

KIPPER: But this will not wait, Professor.

PROFESSOR KUSS: I'm afraid it will have to, Kipper. We are soon to enter ultra-Rocket warp drive.

The Ark is seen to flash several times inside (we need exceptional special effect for this. In comparison of BBC Dr Who effects and those used by Stanley Kubrick I

*would hope that there is some middling ground.) Kuss
strains with control stick and Kipper and Anja are tossed
like leaves in wind.*

The flashing stop. Professor Kuss laugh.

PROFESSOR KUSS: There we are, Kipper. Steady as she go!
(He talk with good cheer). Now, what is problem?

KIPPER (re-adjusting pince-nez): I have been picking up
signal from planet Earth.

PROFESSOR KUSS: Ah yes, little rock which revolve around
sun between Venus and Mars. It is pleasant place. I
went there once as boy. But wait! How Earthlings
send signal? In Earth years it is only . . . *(he presses
buttons on panel in control lever)* . . . 1935. They should
not yet be capable to send signal.

KIPPER: Exactly, Professor. This was signal from *Elves.*

Close-up of look of horror on Kuss face.
CUT TO BLACKNESS

Some Robotic Machines

Suggestions for appearance of machines in *Blast Off!*

The Mighty Ark

This machine based on biblical Ark (as used by Noah,
wife and animals) or even Ark of Covenant. It often
appear in disguise, for example as oil drum or lamp post.
This is, I believe, substantial improvement on Tardis as
appears in *Dr Who*, which look like ancient Victorian
police box. Within Ark is control lever like giant pole
which only Professor Kuss can manipulate.

Elf Trap
A box like rabbit hutch to be deploy on Martian surface. Elf enters through little hole in top thinking he has come home (for Elf trap is looking similar to Elf burrow). In drawing you can see that Elf Trap has appearance of mound of earth. I suggest employing plastic grass like which greengrocer use to brighten up fruit stall.

Elf Jet Pack
I have made scale model using painted banana and silver foil. Photograph is indicative – as model is strapped to back of my puppy.

Kipper Bowl
Kipper has robotic dog bowl. This is oval dish with electronic wires beneath – and many little door which open to reveal secret weapons (sonic bone, etc) similar to James Bond. It also has wheels to be summoned remotely via radio signal. If in dire need (as our heroes sometimes will find selves!) Kipper can summon robotic bowl to rescue. Bowl will also contain strong rope, foot springs (so Kipper and Professor Kuss can bounce above walls) and special gases which sometimes leak out and make havoc on Ark.

Thermo Suit
Mars is cold place unless you are elf. I have design thermo suit in manner of Michelin man (using ring of cotton wool) and dressed statue in picture (enclosed) to

show effect. Please note: this is statue of St Jude with staff (only one available at time of photographing) not image of Professor Kuss.

12 September 1969

Dear Mr Czerkiak,

Although I most sincerely appreciate your interest, I have to confess that your knowledge of Science Fiction clearly outweighs mine! I would suggest that you approach a reputable agent, who I am sure will give your work the attention it deserves.

Bravo for the cricket reference, by the way! Hope there's more of that kind of thing out there, if you know what I mean.

Yours sincerely,
Patrick Moore

PRINCIPLES OF PROPAGANDA

22 September 1985

Dear Uncle Kasimir,

Well, here I still am after one whole year and I'm watching the paint dry on the picture you've hopefully received in one piece along with this letter. I got a First for it. For the whole project, actually. I hope you don't mind being part of a project! It'll need to stand for at least another week before I wrap it, so it can dry properly, but things are so hectic here that I thought I'd write this letter while I found myself with five minutes free.

Wow! That's all I can say. I love being here. It's been a bit of a dream for me so far. And I wouldn't be here at all if it wasn't for you. A girl couldn't ask for a more wonderful uncle, really. Do you know that?

I'm trying to think my way into the latest project they've set us. This term's all about 'Messages and Meaning', and any thoughts you have would be really, really welcome. It's all supposed to be about propaganda, but my tutor's so vague I still haven't got much of an idea what he's on about. I mean, I know what propaganda is, but I don't really know what he wants us to do. The brief says that we're supposed to pretend we're in charge of a country and need to make the people believe in something we want to do. See what I mean? Vague!

Oh well, I don't have too much news. I just wanted you to know that I'm back here in one piece for the new term and raring to go. Hope you like the picture.

Love,
Gabi
XXX

4 October 1985

My dear Gabi,

I am so glad you are happy. As summer is turning to autumn and the leaves die on the trees I have this morning undertaken an inspection of my ornate residence here in Swiss Alps, only to notice there is much wrong with my ornament. There is moss in my pool, crackling tiles and so on. A filigree of decoration in my lamps is tarnished. The balcony extending from one guest bedroom has slipped and many slates have fallen from my roof, smashed to a thousand pieces on the courtyard tiles. As Gabi may conclude, until the arrival of her letter and gift I have been in a dudgeon.

However, upon reading your letter my heart was rising like a great bridge over the River Thames to accommodate a ship with the tallest mast and a sail flapping from the breeze, with spirits ascending in mind of a cuckoo (even in autumn). My darling, my favourite niece, this picture is a work of profound genius, ripe from symbolic mystery. 'Who is this noble gentleman dress as Pope?' I asked upon tearing away your wrapper. 'Who is this man with nimble hound, St Peter key, holy crown and prick ears? It is Kasimir and his faithful dog, Anna Karenina III.' As Anna is proud of face, so too I am proud of you, my Gabi. Now I am knowing why you want so many photographs from me. Please remember that I am your Uncle Kasimir, to whom you should turn in time of trouble or need. I am full of delight that so small gift to you last year has reap such bountiful reward, and honoured to be subject of this masterpiece, in playful modern tradition, by future Picasso, but woman – as is Anna Karenina.

'Bravo,' Anna say. 'Bravo, Gabi. I am imp of perverse.'

So, of propaganda. But first of tutor. You say that he is vague. Vague? What is vague? Vague tutor is like broken road-sign, spinning in wind to give many directions, none true. Perhaps one is true, but as tutor revolve who is to know? When I was youthful, my own estimable tutor, Kuss, would occasionally prick Mongol dagger into desk for emphasis of specific point – on one occasion instructing servant to fire cannon outside class-room windows in case I forget date of nationalistic celebration. All windows smash but even now I remember this date and subsequent ear-whistling from exploded shell.

Perhaps tutor feel that vagueness become him as artist; or that great artist like Gabi does not need telling what to do. This man is idiot. Kuss was remarkable artist and never vague. He was Renaissance Man, superior combination from Machiavelli, Medici and Michelangelo, venerate by artistic community throughout Europe for unparallel application of science in art: of perspective and chemical undertone.

For example, I will tell you of my first experiencing Art. As infant I did of course pay regard to many family portraits hanging in halls and stairwells of family home, often sombre works to keep in with respective dignity. Portrait of my father, great military general; and of his father, renown swordsman; and of his father before him, painted from memory of those who knew him following unspeakable desecration of corpse after battle, all hung in long line of wall outside library. I tread in terror when passing such majestic images, feeling all eyes of history on my head.

However it was not until eighth birthday that Kuss begin commencing formal artistic education. I arrive for lessons early that day, as instructed, and was full of wonder to regard through open doorway that my classroom had been newly decorate overnight in manner of Roman Temple. Kuss was nowhere to be seen. I stand obedient in hallway gazing on to marble columns and great hanging drapes, grape bowl and beyond through window to clear blue sky with mysterious birds suspend in air.

This scene of tranquillity it soothe me, making still butterfly heart, so familiar on approach of daily encounter with Kuss. I did not sweat. My breath it did come easily as inhalation on spring morning amid blossom. What beauty, I think. I imagine my father instructing workmen to complete work between nightfall and day break on pain of terrible retribution.

'Ah, Kasimir.' Familiar voice of Kuss sound from behind me like breath of panther in tree. 'I see you are here on time. Bright and early. Good boy.'

'Yes, sir,' I say, afraid to turn around in case somehow this happy greeting turn like milk in thunder.

'And what do you think of new surroundings?' His breath fall on my collar like curling vapour of London smog and all previous repose was vanish. My heart begin to beat as army marching to attack.

'Sir, the classroom is so nice.'

'Nice?' he whisper. 'What is *nice*?'

I did not know how to reply.

'Well, Kasimir?' I hear tap-tap of his cane on polished floorboards. 'I am waiting.'

'For contemplation,' I say. 'Restful and thoughtful to aid scholastic mind.'

'Very good.'

I stand in silence while he tap cane like dentist point on teeth, as fearful dripping of my sweat.

'And would Kasimir like to sample new environment?'

'Yes, sir.'

'Very well. Go ahead.'

Like piglet who find door to slaughterhouse ajar I did rush forward – but to meet with blinding pain as I collide with rough, unforgivable surface similar to brick wall. My nose crack and break and I fall backward with shriek, collapsing on to hard floor where my head was hit. I lie in blood.

For one moment there was silence, only to be broken by uproar of laughter – not one single voice but many: my father and my mother, Captain Lasiewicz who all call Lasi (once great captain of military regiment, now simple in the head from shard of anarchist grenade which entered brain. In his kindness my father did retain Lasi as family gardener, although he chase after leaves, and he teach me about birds from songs playing on sailor squeeze-box), all kitchen staff, and viper hiss of Kuss. Above me ceiling did spin as bright stars flash in my eyes, iron taste of blood in my mouth.

One hand grip my shoulder and lift me from floor as broken doll, to be hold at armlength, feet above ground so I see crowd gather from behind me.

'My son!' It was my father. He laugh and slap thigh with free hand, face red as boil about to burst. 'You are fool – such fool. If your nose was not already snap I would snap it for you! Did you not see birds hang still in the air? Do you not look?' He laugh, free from all control, arm shaking me upwards and downwards so I became sick, a cocktail.

'Kasimir,' it was Kuss. 'Today you have learned most valuable lesson.'

My father dangle me in direction of classroom, take single step forward and kick at open doorway. With mighty shudder this scene of temple collapse backwards – a painting board – to reveal old classroom.

Kuss continue: 'You did today witness power of Art. Mystery of image. Through image we can manipulate men, Kasimir. Remember this. All things are never what they seem. If you choose to look carefully at scene you would have notice clues I paint so you might avoid humiliation and pain: birds, leaf suspended in midair, water pouring from jug. However, your mind was govern, as ever, by heart.'

So it is, Gabi, that I learn 'Message and Meaning' of art. To Kuss all art was propaganda.

I hope that this gives you some idea of how to proceed. In past times many great leader did regard propaganda as fairy boy politic to their detriment. My own father was to say late in illustrious life that energy he expand through cutting thrust of battle might have been better spent with cunning use of advertisement.

Perhaps this is good place for you to start. I would suggest you look into subject and furnish me in due course with ideas you plan for project. Tell me what is use of propaganda? And once more, thank you for this wonderful painting of Kasimir and Anna Karenina, which is beautiful, rich in significance.

All of my love,
Uncle Kasimir
X

10 October 1985

Dear Uncle Kasimir

I hope that you are well and that your household repairs have all gone smoothly. You must tell me where you've hung the painting. I know it's a long time since I last made a trip to Switzerland, but sometimes I feel like I know every inch of your house from your letters.

Thanks so much for your story about Kuss and your father. I know how much you respect them, but don't you think they could be very cruel sometimes? Anyway, I got your point straight away and started looking at some adverts. It's all about making the people you want to be on your side, or to buy your products, feel good about themselves by believing in what you say, isn't it? I think that's how propaganda works. I looked at some photographs of Mussolini dashing about – apparently he was a bit fat and didn't dash anywhere. But he wanted people to think he was dynamic, and could make great changes in Italy. So he made sure people photographed him looking active. I mean, it wouldn't have been the same if someone had got a shot of him with his feet up scoffing a pizza, would it?

I also looked at some posters for cigarettes and saw the same kind of thing going on. All those men dressed up in cowboy suits looking cool and healthy. You wouldn't want a shot of someone coughing their lungs out down the pub, would you? It's all about controlling the message: vote for me, buy this, buy that, filtering out all the stuff you don't want people to know. No one's going to vote for you if they realise you're evil, or buy your cigarettes if they think they're going to kill them.

How have I done? I hope I haven't rabbited on too much! If there's anything else you can think of, do say. I've got to get cracking soon, though. So if you think I'm going off the rails I'll need to know fast.

Lots of love,
Gabi
XXX

15 October 1985

My dearest Gabi,

I am presently in good health, in spite of a pinhead builder who did manage to disrupt my whole domestic electrical supply while making amends to swimming pool. He reverse his digger into electrical pylon and in consequence I am cold and the evenings are dark, by candlelight, and Anna Karenina snivel under her blanket from fear of ghosted electrical sparking in garden. I will sew builder in court, but of course when I tell him this he did stop working. So nothing changes here. Anna Karenina sniffs in bed, and darkness and dampness and the cold of winter is looming. Perhaps I will come to stay with you in England.

One word here regarding Kuss and my father. You

say they were cruel. This I will not dispute, but sometimes life is cruel. These men prepare me for world they see ahead of them, and this was with best intention. When eventually I realise disappearance of Kuss it was with great regret – never was I able to say goodbye. Never did I know what was to become him. Kuss is gone, my father, great military general, is gone and without them this world is little place. Tiny rock in space which revolve until energy of sun is gone, that is all. Perhaps we will discuss such things when next we meet. It is with heavy heart whenever I think of estimable tutor or my father, giants of men although world still spin – perhaps more slowly.

Now, to better things.

I am most impress with your understanding of propaganda. Perhaps you are aware of my time as undercover agent in Italy during war? On several occasions I talk with Mussolini himself – clever but awful man, not of brains but of fox: full of cunning. He was master of propaganda.

As you tell me, advertising does indeed have so much in common with propaganda. It is propaganda of business, no less. International language of deception, and indispensable for selling. I forget, of course, if you have yet to assume typical student position of hostility in these matters – but should you, then I must tell you that I would agree. It is well known that I am millionaire many times again and again, but I can tell you, my little Gabi, that such good fortune did not arise because of advertising. Source of Kasimir's wealth is s-e-c-r-e-t. (It is in my mind to tell you everything one day, but not today!)

So I must concur with what you think on this matter. Bravo! Only if I may offer one small addition, which you may discover to be invaluable: propaganda as you say is spreading lies for benefit of those who tell the first lie, and like a domino every lie topple one truth: lie, lie, lie. One lie gives birth to similar lie and soon everywhere is lies like ant in dirty kitchen. Germany during war: all was lies. America after war: McCarthy. All is lies. Lie, lie lie. As maker of propaganda (for purpose of college work), one thing to keeping in mind is not lie which say lie about you, but lie which is lie about somebody else – lie of destruction. I shall make this more clear through a second example from youth.

At Easter each year entire family, although not Kuss, did retire to holiday villa in mountain foothill. This was ancient, lonely building enclose in ivy many mile from nearest village of Dasz and reaching only by rutted cart track frequent by vermin. Along track were many tall pine tree and at Easter, family did travel there in line of carts pull by oxen, cow bells ringing, jostle of cutlery and swinging pans, babble of happy children (all brothers and sisters), and Lasi who play sailor squeeze-box with legs dangle from cart pile high with coal for fire. Black like shadow of dust he sing song of wild predatory bird in keep with surrounding desolation.

On such occasion I was sitting silently in first cart next to my father, swathe beneath bison hide, bear furs and musk rat plume. I watch him crack whip and blow steaming breath, many times drinking from leather flask and calling wildly into forest to scare demons, so he say. Should we see elk or similar he would shout to servant in following cart to chase after animal with shotgun, my father shooting beneath servant heels with crossbow to offer encourage. So it was we fill larder for Easter holiday – and with geese, and so on.

However, one Easter, this procession it was halt by giant fallen tree blocking track. At once my father jump from cart, take crossbow and run to bottom end of tree.

'Ha,' he cry, stepping back towards cart, all time watching trees, sharp eyes, like magnetic needle on course to trouble. He did approach cart and hand me crossbow, taking military rifle from behind seat. 'Kasimir, this is time for you to act like man. Hold crossbow ready but do not aim or enemy will act.'

Behind us Lasi did sing haunting melody:

> 'Buzzard is bird with too sharp beak,
> For mouse who squeaking: Eek! Eek! Eek!
> As bird of prey dive high from air,
> And carry mouse to lofty lair.'

This I will always remember.

From behind us my mother call: 'Stanisław, why are we stop?'

'It is nothing, my angel,' father call back, voice firm. 'Merely fallen tree, crashed down in storm. We will

THE WISDOM OF UNCLE KASIMIR

move it presently.' And then he whisper to me, 'Kasimir.
Tree was chop down and hairs on back of my neck
prickle to danger. This is trap, make no mistake.'

'Bandit?' I ask.

'Brigand,' he say with terse nod. Around us wind did
whistle and snow start to fall. 'If we remain here we
possibly also freeze to death.' But he remain jolly, laughing to me and slap my back. He shout to mother: 'Tell ass
of servant to come here with hunting rifle, ho ho.'

In one moment servant arrive standing beside father,
eyes betraying fear. He was of Russian stock.

'Ivan,' my father say, for that was servant name.
'Buckle together like belt or I will blow your own head
from shoulders.'

'But I see tree stump,' he say. 'This is surely trap.'

'Perhaps,' said my father, 'But no worse than one
thousand others I have face before. Remain calm or
much will be the worse for you.'

For this moment servant Ivan appear to stare into
forest, perhaps thinking to flee. But glint barrel of father
rifle did suggest otherwise.

'My son,' say father to me, looking back to cart with
mother and rest of family, 'you are brave boy.' But
suddenly and without warning I see great look of
anguish on his face: 'Wanda!' he shouted at top of voice,
'No!'

I look to see my sister Wanda (your grandmother),
running in play from safety of wagon towards forest. She
babble with laughter and move swift as mink, my

mother unable to catch her. My father he did run too in brave attempt to catch, but too late! From behind tree step brigand deep in common furs (rabbit, weasel, stoat and so on) and holding great hunting knife. He catch Wanda and pull her to him, forcing knife against softy throat.

'Drop down weapons,' he shout.

My mother wail. Father look at her and she cease abruptly.

Lasi stop singing and sailor squeeze-box whine to end like gasp of puncture lung.

'What you say?' my father ask in belligerent tone.

'Put down weapons!' scream brigand like man possess. 'Or I cut girl at throat, ha ha.' He laugh like ghoul and around him from behind forest step army of brigand – ten, twenty I count. Some have knife or axe, one have antique rifle point at us. My father look from one man to next and towards little Wanda, who did struggle and bite at glove.

'This was not our agreement,' my father say, voice full of scorn.

Brigand shook head, lacking in comprehension. 'What are you talking about?'

'Our terms were very clear,' say my father. 'Or are you pinhead?'

Brigand pull Wanda tight towards him, raising knife fraction. 'You are madman,' he say. But I detect quivering uncertainty in voice. I myself did have no idea what my father was meaning, but I say nothing, holding tight to crossbow. Ivan shuffle on spot.

'I say we have agreement,' continue my father.

I see that other brigands did look in confusion at man with knife, for sure leader. One of them say something, but I could not understand, he speak in popular local dialect.

'We have no agreement!' shout brigand. 'What you talk about?'

'You want me to remind you?' ask my father.

'Silence!' say brigand. 'I will kill girl.'

'Ha, little wonder you say I should shut up. That your men would know you have sold them to me.'

All brigands as one did turn to man with knife.

'You lie,' say brigand.

'So you say,' speak my father.

'No! You lie! Now I will kill girl!'

'Wait,' say short brigand in seal hat, placing hand on knife of brigand leader. 'What is this man saying?'

'He tell lies!' shout brigand leader.

'Ha,' say little man in seal hat. 'How do we know this?

'Because I am leader!' Brigand with knife raise voice.

My father did spit at ground. 'He is traitor to you all. Turncoat for blood money. Man who wishes to kill darling little girl, no less. Coward who say I, great military general Stanisław Czerniak, should come with guns to collect brigand posse for reward.'

On hearing name of my father brigands were gasping as one.

But brigand with knife did tug free of little man with seal hat, and swing blade up towards Wanda throat.

However little man knock leader hand to one side and knife fall to ground. Brigand leader stagger back, letting loose of Wanda.

'Run, my child!' shout my father in full throat of voice of war. 'To mother, run!' And from his rifle he let fire both barrels tearing single big hole in head of brigand leader, making all snow in trees red with shower like extraordinary firework rocket. Lasi clap. As Wanda run my father snatch crossbow from me and drop down rifle. 'Load gun, my son!' he shout, jumping on to wagon seat with agility from Cossack blood and firing bolt into heart of brigand who have rifle. Antique gun did detonate upwards into trees scaring crows as black heart of thief spill open as he slump to forest floor and beg in agony. 'Cry, fool!' my father shout. 'You cry so sweetly.' I put bullets from box beside me into breech of rifle and father grab gun back, spinning it on finger like Rooster Cockburn as he fire one barrel then next into brigand crowd. Two men did fall dead in silence as trees for log. He snatch hunting rifle from servant Ivan and let fire special mixing lead shot with great muzzle flash, to pepper remaining thieves. One more man tumble in death throe and others run, full of fear. Swinging hunting rifle about head my father he run after them, pulling own hunting knife from folds of fur overcoat, screaming as devil, strange and awful look on face as I had not seen before, except in tennis tournament at Łódz (another story).

Lasi did reprise singing but I do not remember tune, only mention of eagle.

Later, when my father return, eyes glazing after slaughter and hair damp from sweat, he did speak softly to me. 'Kasimir, to divide is to rule. Convince those who serve your enemy that he is not be trusted, and they will destroy him for you.' He slap Ivan on head with handle of bullwhip for oxen and point to elk among trees. 'Dinner,' he say, and Ivan run quickly after it.

And so you see, Gabi, this is power of persuasion. I hope that my advice is of some use to you and that your project will reach suitable conclusion of you getting excellent grade, as you always deserve. If you wish for me to speak with 'vague' tutor I would be very happy to do this. Perhaps I could even come to England to do so, while house in Switzerland goes under renovations. I would of course wear disguise.

You must tell me how you get on.

All of my love,
Uncle Kasimir
X

29 November 1985

Dear Uncle Kasimir,
Goodness! Grandma never mentioned that story to me once. But when I asked Mum about it on the phone last night she said it was all true. I don't know if she likes you telling me stories like that, though. Oh well, I loved it.

And guess what! I did well with my propaganda project and my tutor says I will get another First. I used everything you said and have included some photographs with this letter so you can see what it was all about. Don't laugh! I thought you'd appreciate the subject.

I hope you've managed to sort out the problems with your house and that you and Anna are both snug for the winter now. I'll be sending you something special for Christmas this year, which I'd better get in the post soon, hadn't I? Time really flies, doesn't it?

Lots of love,
Gabi
XXX

SURVEILLANCE: 1

Editor's note: The purpose of this document and its counterpart ('Surveillance: 2') remains a mystery. To make matters worse, neither is complete – although we are certain that they are separate documents. Both were water-damaged, the top sheets badly pitted and rotted. We have used ellipses to mark points where the text was illegible, and have shown where we have reconstructed incomplete words or sentences; the text ends at the point where Uncle Kasimir's notes were too badly damaged to read. 'Eel' and 'Tractor' remain anonymous beyond the clues relating to their professions and locations. Family gossip suggests a very clear candidate for 'Tractor' but, for legal reasons, we have avoided any such speculation.

Monday, 3 November 1969

Camera √

Ilford film √ (load camera first)

Big torch √

Most little torch √ (+ string)

Large bag √ (three)

Poking stick √

Tool bag √

Rubber glove √ (+ goggle)

Blanket (Anna) √

Blanket (Kasimir) √

Kabanos (Anna) √ (+ water)

Kabanos (Kasimir) √

Toad √ (+ remove squeaker)

Worker overall √ (put on before I leave)

Ruler √   Clipboard √
Stepping ladder √ (secure to roof of car)

6.05 a.m. Location: Street of Eel
Park beyond little trees, hidden but facing house. Quiet
road. House is in darkness. All like [. . .] is in darkness
save for moon. Half moon which is good [. . .] light but
not too much. I have [. . .] most little torch with string
from car roof, so it will dangle over paper pad. So I can
be writing. Car is park in front of house.

6.10 a.m.
Little light come on upstairs. Bathroom? Eel rises.

6.26 a.m.
Other dog walking. Anna barking. I threaten muzzle
from glove compartment [. . .] all of kabanos so she is
very quiet and watch me with beady eye. I wait in
darkness still, imagining all light to come on in house.
Eel, it seem, has poor hearing.

6.30 a.m.
Anna is being bad girl <u>still</u> – she wiggle like spaghetti.
But 1) It is effort of artistic strain from Saturday. 2) She
remain in season. I give her toad to chew.

6.45 a.m.
Anna is sleeping. More lights have come on in Eel house.
Daylight it is break. Activity throughout house of Eel.

7.30 a.m.

Little Eels to school. Rain has started, drumming like [. . .] on car roof.

7.35 a.m.

Eel open side gate for house and lift dustbin on to driveway. Very good. He retreat through side gate and return with what look like pipe-roll, three feet tall. Thick as chimney pot. He check string which is tied to secure roll. Great interest.

7.55 a.m.

Mrs Eel she leave for work, using cheap umbrella.

8.02 a.m.

I see Eel. He approach car and I slip down inside own car. He is hurry and does not see me.

8.04 a.m.

Eel is gone. Slippery Eel. I wait. See neighbour on one side he leave for work with wife. Good. On other side is empty house for sale.

8.10 a.m.

I wait still and [. . .] overalls. Check tool bag items:

Poking stick	Camera
Large torch	Clipboard
Glove	Ruler

8.30 a.m.

In car with notes of clipboard. I transcribe and watch dustmen remove bin (without evidence, all list below, seal in bag in boot. Eel is on hook.). Eel he is too late.

Notation of evidence

Photographic evidence 'A': correspond to image on film roll 'A', from photograph number two on roll. Photograph one it is test image (cat).

Photograph 1:–

Photograph 2–14: extended roll, laid unroll on grass. Roll reveals to be linoleum, cheapest variety, with letter holes cut throughout for stencil. Eel has made competent job of cutting holes – uniform appear. Letters are of following dimension (photograph has ruler beside letter, for size):

N   22″
O $21\frac{1}{2}$″
P $21\frac{3}{4}$″
A $21\frac{1}{2}$″
R $21\frac{3}{4}$″
K $21\frac{1}{4}$″
I   23″
N $21\frac{3}{4}$″
G   24″

Photograph 15, 16, 17: Paint brush with yellow paint trace (from in shed)

Photograph 18, 19: Paint brush with white paint trace.

Photograph 20, 21: Length of string in yellow paint.

Photograph 22–24: Pages from *Daily Express* (Friday, 31 October – date in question, of event) all smear in white and yellow paint.

8:45 a.m. New location: rear of Eel Shop. (Pubic right of way) [. . .]
Eel challenge me. I tell him it is my right to make photograph from public highway. He say he will telephone for polices. I laugh in his face. Eel goes into shop and watch from window with [. . .] mouth obscenity.

Photographic evidence 'B': correspond to image on film roll 'B', from photographic number two on roll. Photograph 1 is test image (dog – not Anna).

Photograph 1: –

Photograph 2–18: Photographic record of individual letter. Letter are again accompanying by ruler, for each one. And of course horizontal – although I have also made place of my shoe to demonstrate scale.

N   22″
O   21½″
P   21¾″
A   21½″
R   21¾″
K   21¼″
I   23″
N   21¾″
G   24″

Photograph 19, 20: Whole words 'No' and 'Parking' – both of these with shoe.

Photograph 21–22: 'Aerial' photograph from stepping ladder – [. . .] location on public highway outside exit to Eel shop (convenient location for parking when shopping in High Street).

Photograph 23: Yellowing line

Photograph 24: Shoe next to Anna to demonstrating scale.

9.10 a.m. Another location

Pause to drink coffee in Maruzi Café next to Boots Chemist (for photographic development) – car parked convenient to rear of Eel shop, on public Highway. I review document record.

9.15

Eel has arrived in Maruzi Café. I note carefully what he is speaking: [. . .]

ONCE UPON SOME STORM STRUCK NIGHT BY KAZIMIERZ CZERNIAK

Once upon some storm struck night, in old room lit by
candlelight
I lift large book from highest shelf and – thud – it hit
the wooden floor.
It fall open on tattered pages, showing beasts in silver
cages
Pages old, they stained with mould, I could not read
them any more.
I stare at book but it too late – I could not read it any
more.
It almost dust down on the floor.

What serendipity this is, I think, while looking at the
mist
That makes its milky moisture into ghouls outside my
study door.
This book of mine I'd thought it lost, but here it is on
floor, star-crossed.
Old childhood text of fairground fancy, ancient ritual
and folklore
I remember book of fairground fancy, ritual and
folklore
That now lies on study floor.

Now it seems so long ago, as I begin this tale of
  woe
About the book that Autumn eve that tumble down
  on to the floor.
All these animals locked in, around me room did start
  to spin
As I saw Anna K within – my one and only true
  amour.
She look at me and 'Help me Kasimir!' her loving
  eyes implore.
        Lying there in book on floor.

What is this? I ask myself, as I look up at shady
  shelf,
Imagining my Anna's soul snipped out by cruel crazed
  claw.
I think of this satanic spanner, O my poor pathetic
  Anna –
Your precious soul from evil book, I vow you I will
  draw.
Cursed to die in picture book, but from it you I
  draw.
        Free again you'll be once more.

On that dark October morning, I could see this was a
  warning,
As the book with Anna caught, it lay there on cold
  study floor.
Outside – moonlight, mist and silence – but in room
  an inky violence,
And my Anna now in chains in pages of terror!
With fairground folk and dusty childhood memories
  of terror!
    Pages lifeless on the floor.

I take from shelf another book, hands trembling like
  the wings of rook.
Can I release my Anna K, my one and only true
  amour?
This is work of desperate devil – he take my puppy
  dog to evil
Pages of a dusty book so she belongs to me no
  more.
O Anna K, O Anna K, be Kasimir's again once
  more!
    Not imprisoned in folklore.

The book it open in my hand, on pages that I
    understand
Will take this vile and deadly curse away from Anna
    K, O Lord.
And my heart go pitter patter – from the attic comes a
    clatter!
Could this be some other evil heading for my study
    door?
What is coming from the attic, beating on the wooden
    floor?
    Devils – arriving by the score?

What is this? Some devils there? Is this them upon the
    stair?
I know not what they want from you, O Anna K my
    true amour.
They're beating now with bile and blight – O fateful
    late October night
I will not – must not – let them in: your poor pale
    prison frame to paw.
You'll be safe my Anna K your image they will never
    gnaw.
    Safe for now upon the floor.

The window pane it start to move; I'm sure I see a
    devil's hoof
O what else do you want from me, now that you have
    my true amour?
My Anna trapped in silver cage, she prisoner within a
    page . . .
Frosty air comes rushing in and lo! I look towards the
    door.
But it comes from window pane. I fall to knees on
    wooden floor.
       O! Lord Jesus! I implore.

I'm holding book in cold-numb hands; I need to find
    ingenious plan
But window it is opening and I see devils by the
    score.
Their hoofs are red, their legs are yellow – O I am
    unlucky fellow.
One leg enters long and scaly and alights on wooden
    floor!
Accursed presence in my room alighting on my
    wooden floor!
       This I never will ignore.

I rise from knees creep quick to corner, in my haste I
    see I've torn the
Page from out of magic book, now I am truly cursed
    for sure.
Will they work, my magic pages – will I rot with
    clumsy mages?
There's no candle in this corner, I will over pages
    pour
In half light as the ghouls grow closer, I will over
    pages pour
        To my Anna's soul restore.

The door it open with a creak; my soul, my spirit,
    growing weak
What is happening? It must be contrary to nature's
    law.
Cold air it is rushing in, O who invited evil djin?
The devils are approaching me, and Anna K still on
    the floor
These devils will not go away – O God I do to you
    implore
        Save me from these spirits' claw!

I cannot see the dusty page, my Anna in enchanted
cage
And here I stand in corner, legs are tremble on the
dusty floor.
O what now do you want from me? I did not summon
these djinni
And all the while my Anna lies in prison on the study
floor
Imprisoned in forgotten book that fell upon the dusty
floor.
      Now a noise comes from the door.

And now over at the window, tapping like a weeping
willow,
Spirits, phantoms all from Hell arriving stealthy by
the score
My room is filling with pure evil. O my love! I hope
that she will
Hang on to her life while quick these ancient pages I
explore
In the half-light, for her life, these ancient pages I
explore
      As ghouls come through my study door.

Suddenly I fall in darkness – what am I, some hollow
    carcass?
The candlelight, once glowing, is now black and
    empty to its core.
What evil breath, what ghostly gust? My memory I
    now must trust.
No longer can I see my only Anna lying on the
    floor.
The light has gone and there's no Anna lying lonely
    on the floor.
        The wind it cry: 'For evermore!'.

In the dark there is a scuffle, in my ears the noise is
    muffled
What has happened to my senses, severed, censored
    evermore?
I can feel the evil finger, on my cheek its cheerless
    linger –
And the flapping of a wing or feather coming from
    the door.
O what did I ever do to earn the wrath of ghouls
    galore?
        I'll live in hope for how long more?

Praying now I clutch those pages, thinking of the
 ancient mages
And their secret wizard's wisdom that will help me
 win this war.
I mutter spells into the darkness: 'Magic take away my
 harness!'
Lo! the wind blows backwards sucking demons from
 the blood-stained floor.
Yes! The wicked spectres are now flying through the
 open door.
     And I am alone once more.

So what to do about my hound, still inside pages she
 impound?
O Anna I am coming for you, you won't have to wait
 much more.
My candle lit with stub of match, my magic once more
 I dispatch
And slowly Anna I make free: released from pages of
 folklore
She curse black hearts of frightful folk who trapped
 her inside old folklore!
     And my Anna lives once more.

SURVEILLANCE: 2

Sunday, 16 August 1970
    Camera √
    Zooming lens √
    Ilford film √ (load camera first)
    Turnip (+ make several turnips, into pieces and in bag)
    Waterproof coat √ (subdue colour)
    Clipboard √

10.45 a.m. Location: near entrance to Tractor farm
Tractor is leaving in Landrover to attend church service.
I wait until Landrover has been left for some five
minutes.

10.55 a.m.
I arrive at Tractor farm and park car at gate to sheep
field. I see sheeps away in distance.

11.00 a.m.
I scatter turnip in field.

11.05 a.m.
Sheeps approach.

11.11 a.m.

One sheep he begin to eat turnip – he have white fur. More sheeps approach.

11.16 a.m.

All of sheeps eat turnip. I record following evidence.

Photographic evidence 'A': correspond to image on film roll 'A', from photo number three on roll. Photograph 1 and 2 is test image using zooming lens, for focus (rabbit on slope). Photograph 1: –

Photograph 2: –

Photograph 3: Sheep with white fur all over.

Photograph 4: Sheep with white fur all over.

Photograph 5–10: Sheeps in group (five sheeps) all with white fur all over.

Photograph 6–8: same as from different view, to show other side of sheeps and proximity to tractor farm – To make sure see these are sheeps belonging to tractor.

Photograph 10–24: Sheeps with red head (variety of angle). Red on horns, too from butting like goat.

Photographic evidence 'B': correspond to image on film roll 'B', from photo number 2 on roll. Photograph 1 is test image without zooming lens.

These images they are to make supplementary evidence in according with those already duly submitted to Royal Motor Insurance [. . .]

Photograph 1: –

Photograph 2: [. . .]

Photograph 3: [. . .]

Photograph 4–16: Denting to door panels of near side of red Volvo Estate (mine, damage).

Photograph 17–18: Further denting to rear, with distant image of red heading sheeps in view, behind.

Photograph 19–21: Red Volvo estate in sheeps field. Sheeps approach in menace.

Photograph 22–24: Tractor return in Landrover.

[. . .]

Editors' note: the rest of the document is illegible.

MY SCOTTISH HOLIDAY

16 August 1986

It is many years since I have enjoyed a holiday and today I did embark on one to Scotland with my neighbour Erwin (not Rommel, but German) and his wife Ursula. I will resolve to keep a clear note of each day, day by day, to make for once a proper use of journal. It has been my experience that Erwin and Anna are not afflicted by typical German characteristic inflexibility and rudeness. Erwin is Professor of Aesthetic and sculptor of international renown. Ursula paints.

Anna Karenina is to remain at house in Swiss Alps, cared for by my assistant Greta. In her youth Greta will be able to take Anna for far longer walks, and to throw many more sticks than can I. Consequently I feel some sadness, but in light of rabies disease, and so on, for Anna to accompany me would be wrong.

It was my decision not to mention this holiday to relatives in Great Britain. Since 1981 they have decided not to visit me, and so I shall not go to them. Naturally if my Gabi had not sent me postcard saying she was also on artistic holiday in Paris I would have arranged to see her, but only her.

17 August

In Glasgow. Flight was terminal. This city is like wet rag left hanging from oily pipe. Dark, full of rainwater. Ursula is incapable of intelligent conversation – of any conversation. Until today I did not recognise this as it has been habit of Erwin to talk constantly. I did not realise this, also, until today. Throughout our flight he speak rubbish about artist funding and she say nothing. Tomorrow we travel to Highland in hiring car, which Erwin say he will drive. He insist on <u>large</u> vehicle, <u>heavy</u> vehicle.

'Like tank?' I say.

He look at me with cool eye. Ursula is silent – surprise, surprise.

'Why not flighty sport model?' I suggest.

Erwin pooh pooh this suggestion and retire to bed with headache, leaving me to enjoy company of Ursula, who is nauseous, in hotel bar. She proceed to read book, *Ivanhoe*, in silence. At seven o'clock I telephone Greta from payphone at bar to enquire upon Anna. Anna is in fine health, romping all day in field with neighbouring Dachshund, she say.

'What Dachshund?' I ask. 'There is no Dachshund.'

'Dachshund with long hair from next door.'

'There is no Dachshund with long hair next door and neighbours are with me in Glasgow, here.'

Ursula, she speak, overhearing conversation: 'I know this Dachshund. It is belonging to my nephew Ralphie who has come to cut hedges.'

I instruct Greta to wait by telephone – that I will call her back regarding Dachshund.

'Ursula,' I say, lighting cigar, 'what is this about hedges?'

'Oh?' she reply. 'Did Erwin not mention this to you?' She study book, eyes failing to meet with mine – whether from stupidity or cunning I did not know.

'No, he did not.'

'Oh,' she say, as if I was telling her matter of no importance.

'Please tell me about Ralphie, hedges and Dachshund,' I ask her.

'Ralphie is going to trim down hedge which is running alongside our property. His little dog Petal always travel with him.'

'Petal?'

'Ralphie is artist, from Berlin.'

I say nothing for some time, making significant pause. 'And why,' I ask her at length, 'is artist performing garden surgery?'

'Did Erwin not tell you?'

'No,' I say, anger building in me like steam in piston. 'Perhaps you would be so kind as to tell me.'

'Why,' she say, still examining the book, 'Ralphie is making artistic sculpture from hedge with funding through European Social Fund, for common heritage.'

'From hedge?'

'From hedge. Now you must excuse me, please, as I am more nauseous than earlier.' She retreat to bed, clamber on stair like beetle.

I telephone Greta once more and ask her whether hand of darkness has yet fallen over Swiss Alps – I fear that in two ways this might be so.

'No, Kasimir, dusk is falling but not yet darkness.'

'Please,' I ask her, 'will you go on to the balcony of the main living room and look directly to the left, at a hedge adjoining neighbouring property. Do you know this hedge of which I speak?'

'Tall, verdant green hedge, so lush, beautiful to eye,' she say. 'Yes, I know this hedge. Perhaps this is the finest hedge in all of Switzerland.'

'Good. Will you please go and look now.'

'Now?' She speaks confused.

'Right now. I will make further telephone call to you shortly, in ten minutes.'

I replace telephone and asked barman for whisky.

'Aye, an' will sir be stayin' with us fer long?' he ask me in local dialect. I understand Scottish tongue from wartime experiences with brave men of Highlander regiment, but am not able to write this well, although I attempt.

'We leave tomorrow,' I tell him.

'Are ye gen awa lang?'

'Possibly Switzerland,' I say.

He laugh, thinking I joke. 'An whitsa ruffle yer feathas?'

'I am not bird,' I tell him. He leave me in peace as I fume over 'dram' (Scottish serving of whisky).

Ten minute pass and I call Greta once more. She

answer telephone immediately and clear throat. In background I hear Anna whine. This is not good, I think.

'Kasimir,' she say. 'What surprise.'

'What?'

'I mean, how good to speak to you.' Her voice quiver like teeth of comb.

'What is this?'

'Hello?'

'Greta!' I shout. 'Are you pinhead?'

'Oh . . . Kasimir.'

I pause and finish whisky. 'Tell me about hedge.'

'Maybe it could wait until you return?'

I say nothing and count in head to ten, as my father told me he did before firing first shot in Russian insurrection.

'No,' I say. 'Tell me now.'

'Oh Kasimir.'

Anna, she whimper – long sound like last note of flute as orchestra die.

'What?'

'Is simply awful.'

I think. Is this awful for me, elderly millionaire who Greta complain has outdating conservative value? Or is this awful to Greta, attractive young student from internationally recognise Swiss School for girls, who has travelled world and work as Chalet Maid throughout winter before hasten into my employ?

'What?' I ask.

'Oh.' Silence.

'Tell me.'

'It is . . . maleness.'

I say nothing, preferring not to hear her words. In fact I did not understand words

'What?' I ask again at length.

'It is male . . . shape. And woman shape. Breast.'

'I see.' I am, however, speechless. I do not want to see this shape of male in Swiss Alp abutting property, with breast, visible from balcony of my own main living room. I cannot in any way imagine.

'Oh,' I tell her. 'So. I see. Now listen to me. This is work of pervert artist of Berlin calling himself Ralphie, owner of dog called Petal, who is Dachshund with who my Anna play.'

'Oh dear.' She sound full from tears.

'Please, little Greta, do not cry. I would ask you instead to do this thing for me. Call good friend Otto of mine – his number it is in telephone book on table before you. Otto Bechte. Do you see this?'

She snuffle: 'Yes, I see book. Yes, Bechte. Otto Bechte.'

'Otto will assist us in this matter. He is old friend. Please telephone him and tell him that I am asking you to call and it is urgent matter. Ask him does he remember Grocer of Stalingrad? He will of course remember. Say that we have one more Grocer and would he please attend to him for me in similar fashion as in Stalingrad. Ask him if he will do so tomorrow. I will telephone tomorrow night and learn what has happened. Will you do this?'

'I will,' she say. 'I am so sorry this has happening.'

'My little Greta,' I tell her. 'You must not mourn.'

'No, Kasimir.'

I tell her goodbye, ask barman for one more whisky and toast my good friend Otto, Butcher of Stalingrad. (Recently he move into isolated cabin also in Swiss Alps to cure depression from burden of wartime deed.)

18 August

Erwin and Ursula attend morning breakfast in uneasy quiet.

'Good day,' I tell them – making joke. For outside it is of course rain.

Erwin look at me in nerves. 'About hedge,' he say.

'Hedge?' I ask, making pretence of ignorance. 'Oh, hedge!'

'Yes,' say Erwin. 'I am so sorry nothing was said.'

'Why?' I reply, in attitude of frivolity. 'Why should anything be said about hedge? It is only hedge, ha ha. In Poland we would make foot-mat from hedge.'

Erwin brighten at once. Ursula beam as if told she is beautiful woman or similar (she is not).

'Ho ho,' Erwin laugh to me. 'What silly misunderstanding.'

'How silly, yes,' I answer.

And so we all laugh over pot of tepid tea and kipper.

'Now,' I say, 'we have holiday to enjoy.'

Afternoon

So we drive in a Mercedes car which I choose over hill and glen to town of Perth and from there to Braemar where Queen is in situ. Along route we see many animals:

Long hair cow
Rabbit (many of them)
Small deer
Toad
Sheeps
Small beast who move like pencil over road

In Braemar Ursula want to take photograph of insipid Royal children (of German descent) while Erwin prefer to visit clothe shop to look for deer-stalking hat, such as worn by great Sherlock Holmes, master of detection, creation of Conan Doyle. I resist temptation to tell him how stupid is this and what fool he will look.

And onward to Ballater. Little village in shadow of hills with beautiful church, fine bakery Leith and Strachan of Royal Deeside grocer. This 'grocer' make me chuckle, although later fidget somewhat in coffee shop at apprehension. I wonder if perhaps I was acting in haste to alert Otto. He is very lovely man, although unpleasant. Enrage by sculpture of hedge (male and female shape) could I have act too far, in asking Greta to telephone him and resolve situation?

While Erwin and Ursula enjoy local fare of buttery, bap, jam and scone I remove myself to telephone box near village green to make expensive call once more to Swiss Alps.

'Hello?' Greta was breathless.

'Greta, hello.'

'Kasimir!' she shout.

'Greta, what is?'

She begin to talk fast, full with excite. 'I did call Otto, who come first thing in this morning with van. What a nice man.'

'He can be a very nice man,' I say, although thinking that he can be unpleasant, also.

'Well, Kasimir, you will be pleased in hearing how hedge is no more problem.'

'Oh? How is this?'

'Good friend Otto speak to artist Ralphie and together they remove whole hedge with flaming thrower.'

'Flaming thrower?'

'Yes, all of hedge is burned and Ralphie has spent afternoon cleaning ash and soot away. Otto has in kindness agree to look after Petal while Ralphie do this, and has gone away in van, perhaps to buy juicy bone.'

'How very kind,' I say. 'Very good. This is all I need to know.'

'Otto send you his regards. He is very nice man.'

'Thank you, Greta. This is all good news.'

I said goodbye to her, replace the telephone, and retire to church green to watch spectacle of Highlands dancing, to the company of bagpipe. Rain did stop for short while and sun break through. The contemplation of nature.

All the time I smile. Petal dog will get many juicy bone, because Otto I know love dog of any sort. He owe his life to spaniel kennel in Stalingrad where he did eat all dogs to avoid starvation and now he see each one as friend. One time I ask him if he saw also in every dog a meal, and he shook head grave. For man possessing of such fond countenance it is always so strange to see darkness of shadow which cross his face, sorrow in eyes, on thoughts of unsavoury nature.

'In war,' he tell me, 'People do thing they would forget. You know this, Kasimir. All kinds of life were laying down for another.'

Of course I do know this.

Since war Otto did become veterinary surgeon and has saved many animal life. Medical instrument and drug exert to him fascination from wartime activities in art of interrogation, but in all is for common good. Therefore I am grateful to learn artist 'Ralphie' from Berlin was in physical state to clear up hedge remnant after meeting Otto. In days of old, Otto could remove entire set of one man's teeth and certain bones without his knowing until anaesthetic wore away. Such was skill of persuasion.

And onward to fish fly on River Dee – same tomorrow.

19 August
I catch a salmon with a fly. A little fly of wire and hair with beady eye, and a hook. What skill is contain within simple art of man who make fly.

20 August

Erwin had telephone call from nephew Ralphie this evening, and he did stand in deerstalker hat and shout to me from doorway of hotel room.

'Only yesterday we catch fish. Now I am learning you did direct this vandalism – or do you deny so?'

I sigh and smoke cigar. 'Take hat from pinhead,' I tell him. 'It does not become you. Was it I who wait until Scottish Holiday to make perversion in hedge?'

'We make art,' he rage at me. 'Public Art.'

'What rubbish,' I say to him. 'This was perversion of natural beauty, from theft of public purse.'

'Philistine,' he call me. So I shrug and slam door on face. He leave with Ursula and I telephone home from comfort of hotel room, speak to Anna and sing her merry hunting song until she sleep.

21 August

My holiday continue without Teutonic influence. Today I travel to Loch Garten to see Osprey.

There is RSPB hide, which is excellent for bird. I have superior binocular and regard envy of fellow watcher. I see too Siskin and Greenfinch. And one red squirrel, which hop along branch above my head to dance in sunlight.

22 August

Today I meet Moses, a pig.

A Bird Hide

I have for many years made study of bird in field and, like other men with concern in field of ornithology, spend many hours making note and sketch observation of bird from sparrow to eagle. But what of precise art of watching bird? Who has spent necessary time examining science of observation? I ask following question: from which elevation is best to watch birds? Above or below?

Should bird hide be on ground or in tree (tree-house, perhaps hiding in trunk of tree, as King Charles II)?

What material is best to conceal watcher? Glass or fabric, perhaps muslin? Soft non-reflecting surface or surface to contain noise and smell of human.

Relate to (3): process of extracting human smell from hide without blowing on to bird. And what of bird and smell? A bird does not need smell to hunt food, but it can smell. (All bird have olfactory nerve.) But bird cannot speak, so we cannot ask one how well it smell. Answer? Sufficient testing to seeing parameter of human scent mix with bird, and to deduce distance from bird of hide, direction of smell flow and quality of surface material.

Noise prevent. All in hide must muffle slippers – or floor to be padding with wool, or similar. Wool it become so dirty, like sheeps fur, unless beneath cover of durable material.

Camera hole? What size of hole for lens? Lens hole might be present even in glass enclosure.

(Editors' note: this entry was accompanied by a detailed plan of Kasimir's proposed bird hide.)

23 August

Unpleasant but amusing telegram from Erwin. He say he will 'get to bottom of matter'. As I know who is bottom (Otto) I would not advise to do this. I telephone Greta and tell her to maintain detailed record of movement next door.

(Editors' notes: 1. Could this perhaps be a reference to the 'Surveillance' documents? 2. There is a drawing of a sow standing beside a man on this page.)

24 August

More rain. In afternoon I return to Royal Deeside and visit Lochnagar. As I arrive rain clear. I admit this to be place of outstanding beauty. I walk perimeter of Loch and cast stones to depth, staring up to mountain top lost in mist. I believe Scottish Highland to have special magic in touch with real artistic soul: solitary sound of wind through heather, taking sweet scent to me and smell of stone, moss, rain.

Unusual Episode

As afternoon draw forward rain it return, but more heavily. So at seven I set forth to my hotel for night. After short distance I pull over to study map and consider best route home. I am tired and in longing for my bed.

Driving on mist thicken and I find myself going upwards, up, ever up. I glimpse pinewood tree on both side of road and glitter of deer eye from headlight – wink as road narrow.

Driving so slowly I listen to sound of car tyre on road, passing through puddle and crunch on grit; how she suck on mud. This mist was grow more thick, like smoke drift over road from burning on either side, when I see dark shape straight in front of me, tall shape and I hit foot on brake – I skid, spin in carousel and strike head.

For one moment all was blackness, until I hear a knocking – tap tap. This was hard sound like which I could not picture. I feel coldness to one side of head and open eyes, realising I am nestle with cheek against cool window of car door.

I cry out! In front of me a fist. I raise one arm in defence, other to cross on chain around neck – so small but still like blade; little dagger. But fist it did not hit me.

'Hello?' Voice was calling me. Scottish voice, soft, of a man. He tap again on windscreen. 'Are you all right, sir?'

'What?' I reply with militaristic determination. I curse my luck at skid and uncharacteristic display of weakness and confusion.

'Looks like you have hit head.'

'Excuse me?' I ask and open door, stepping from car with authority. Immediately I hear how quiet all about me is. Rattle of wood as bird take flight somewhere; hiss of little stream close by – no, I look down. Just visible through twirling mist is ditch by edge of road, flood out by rain.

I look up at stranger who knock on my window. Squat man of fifty years with black hair slick back through grease and moon face, no neck, and great stomach beneath long overcoat. I cannot see eyes behind pebble sunglasses; and in all this shape, he look to me like small Buddha.

'Good evening,' he say quietly, his voice soft Scottish but high pitch, purr like cat in balloon of helium.

'Good evening, sir,' I reply, offering hand. He lift arm in return and I see black leather glove, cold to touch and hard stitch along finger as he grip me. Around us I see nothing – barely branch. I feel shiver on spine but stand firm. Something of this man it is peculiar.

'A shame about the car,' he say, indicating with glove hand at Mercedes. I had not yet notice that front of car was crumple like tin can kick by young boy. I examine damage and conclude car will not drive.

'Won't get you very far,' he say. 'Pity.'

'I see something in road,' I reply, 'and so I brake.'

'A deer, perhaps?' He shift preposterous sunglasses down nose so I see little dark eyes.

'Not deer,' I say. 'This was great, dark shape.'

'Deer are awfae big around here, sir.'

'That may be.' I look again at car. Is wreck. Water fizz and drip from radiator, running to make steaming puddle on road. 'But I cannot see what I hit.'

'Aye,' he say. 'That can happen. If it was a deer, maybe the poor creature hauled itself away tae die in the trees. You cannae see in this weather. You just cannae see.' His tongue make little clicking noise, tip poking from lips while he speak. I imagine his mind like small wheel and cog, turning independent while he converse with me.

But he speak truth. Grey wall of mist all around, only several branches poke here and there. I look at road but see no blood. No sign of dragging. I rub my hand on my face and feel moisture on skin from mist.

'Bad weather for time o' year,' he say. 'Makes roads so slippery.'

'Most inclement,' I tell him. Water drip from hidden leaves.

'And you are long way from hame.'

'Oh?' I answer. 'You seem to know lot.'

'Oh, no. But only person living in neck o'woods is me.'

'I see. I apologise. Crash has made for me headache.' In truth, he give me willy.

'So whit we gan tae do?' he ask me, his voice like lonely gull.

'I shall call AA breakdown service.'

'Oh, aye, well. There's a wee problem with that, sir.'

'Problem?'

'Aye,' he say. 'There's nae phone around here. Nae phone an' nae folks, neither.'

'In this case, perhaps you can give me lift to nearest garage?'

'Aye, well. I would. But I havnae car. An I would say ye could walk, but it's an awfae, awfae long way to go. Too far for man on foot.'

I feel greatest unease.

'Now,' he say, 'What I would suggest is f'r you to mak yoursel' at hame at ma wee place until the mornin'. Then the postie he comes by with ma milk an the post. Same time every day, nine on th' dot. An' he'll give ye a ride tae town.'

I consider this and realise I have no choice. My head throb from hitting and car was wreckage. What was I to do? Remain in car whole night? Already it was late and darkness would soon fall over mist making double darkness.

'Leave your things in car, sir. They'll be safe enough behind a locked door.' He laugh, short sound like cough. 'Aye, ye had better lock the door.'

I turn key in lock.

'Follow me, then, sir.'

'My name is Kasimir.'

'Aye, sir, that's fine.'

He turn fast, bottom of coat rise out around him like flower, and walk away with haste. I follow as good as I am able, some steps behind. He turn to right and hop over ditch and proceed up path in tree. As he walk his feet they make clicking noise like tongue, and around us, close then far, and close once more, I hear sound. Jingle sound of metal.

'What is this sound?' I ask him.

'Oh, that is my hound. He wander in trees – just collar rattling as he wander.'

'I see.' I look back for car and see nothing, only mist – darkness of mist. I could barely see pathway at my own feet and sometimes I stumble. In front of me his back bob like thing in liquid, round shoulder while he hurry onward.

We reach house in darkness, little place with low door so I stoop to enter. Man reach about inside doorway for some moments, while I listen to tick-ticking of clock. He strike match, put flame to lantern and I find myself in one big room, embers of fire which glow, and armchair on either side. Second door led to what was probably kitchen and at far end of room was staircase. He place lantern on little table in middle of room.

'Please sit down,' say man, bending by fireplace and blowing breath on to cinders. He throw kindling wood from basket on to ember and small flame crackle up. 'My name is Uncle Donald.'

'As I say, I am Kasimir.' I sit on armchair to left of fireplace. 'So, you have nephew and niece? I have many.'

'No, I have none,' he say.

I shift uncomfortable in seat.

'You are not from these parts?' he ask me.

'No,' I say. 'I live in Swiss Alps.'

'But you are not Swiss?'

'No, I am of Polish Extraction.'

He nod. 'Would you like drink?'

'You are most kind,' I say.

He take off coat and hang on back of door. Beneath he wear smart tweed suit.

'You are living here by yourself?' I ask.

'With dog,' say he, walking across room to small

cabinet. He open door and take out two tumbler glass. 'Listen,' he say, looking upward.

I listen. Above us I hear patter of paws, knock-knock of claw on wood.

'That's him up there,' say Uncle Donald.

As if to confirm, I hear jangle of collar. Did dog enter house with us? I did not remember. Perhaps dog have his own way in.

I nod as Uncle Donald go away to kitchen and return with whisky bottle.

'It's all I have,' he say, voice husky now, something of whisper.

While he pour drink, I examine surrounding: small table with one chair in corner of room, bowl of fruit with apple upon it; painting of lake with island above fireplace, dark clouds in sky. Old clock on mantelpiece, pendulum which swing for ticking like old man finger pointing down. Room have one window next to front door with curtain drawn.

'The wind's getting up,' he say, offering me glass.

'Indeed,' I answer. Outside steady rush of air gasp at cottage walls. 'Do you think this will be storm?'

'Oh, aye. Maybe it will.' He sit down in armchair opposite me and look on to fire, crackling now, flame jumping although room it still oddly cold. 'Well, well,' he say, sipping whisky from tumbler. Gust of wind puff from chimney sending spark on to old, worn rug at feet. He stamp it, throw log on to fire and position guard in front. 'We dinna want to burn.' He sit back in armchair and nod, removing sunglasses from face. Speaking slowly, almost in whisper, he rub eyes: 'There. Now.' He blink. Eyes are small, pupil large. He finish drink and pat hands over stomach. 'Well.' He take watch from top pocket and examine time, expressionless. Clock it tick on mantelpiece. He look from one to the other and then nod, lick lips.

'That is bruise you have on head,' he say.

'It ache,' I reply.

'Dear me.'

'Tell me,' I ask him. 'What do you do for living here, all alone? Farmer perhaps?'

'Oh no, no, no,' he say, voice descending from whisper almost to silence with each word. 'Nothing like that.'

'Oh?'

Fire crackle, log burn. But still no heat. I shiver.

'No, I am story-teller,' he say.

'Writer?' I ask. Silence. I wait for him to speak, but he only look at me, stroking fingertip over smooth cheek – what smooth skin he have entirely. Smooth skin, but not so pink. Pale skin.

'Something like that,' he reply. 'Something similar. But, no, I never write my stories down.'

I feel wind from chimney; it make whistle. Above us thud – patter of feet. Thud again. Uncle Donald look up. 'He'll just be shifting from the draft. It's an auld, auld place I have. An auld, auld place.'

Lamp flicker on table, unsteady for one moment, making shadow shift on wall. I clear throat and drink whisky in one gulp. Uncle Donald nod and stand up, fetch bottle and place on stool between us. 'Please help yourself,' he say.

I pick up bottle and notice it has no label. He see me and understand. 'An auld, auld bottle,' he tell me. 'An auld, auld bottle.'

'I see.' I uncork bottle and fill glass. He hold out glass and I do likewise with his own.

'You are writer who does not write anything down?' I ask, moving feet.

'No,' he reply soft, so softly. Almost the wind drown over voice. 'I am just story-teller. Very ancient profession.'

'And this does pay you much?'

He shrug. 'I could tell you story,' he say.

'Story?' I answer. 'I like story. On occasion I have also written story: adventure, television drama and so on.'

'Very good,' he say, watching me so close. 'I like man who knows way around words.'

'That is me,' I say.

'Very good,' he reply.

'So you will tell me story? This would be suitable way to spend stormy night in Scottish Highland.' I laugh.

He nod, lips close. 'So,' he say. 'A story.' He lean back in armchair and I do similar. He close eyes, place hands on lap and, like this, he begin. 'A story,' he say again.

'Yes,' I reply.

'You want me to tell you a story. I suggest you shut your eyes.'

I close my eyes.

This is what happen when he tell me his story – word for word, as closely as I do remember, although without Scottish accent.

'The wind was howlin' through trees. It was a cold, fearful night, dead in the middle o' winter. Through forest, save for sound of wind, awful wind ripping at branches, scouring leaves from every last twig, was only silence. Nothing was moving except those things blown, tugged or thrown by wind. Dead leaves tumble over ground. Rag caught on wire fence flap, torn like flag at end of battle. Above all this full white moon burn hole in sky; sky dark as pitch it seemed to those unlucky to be looking upwards. And of those there were very few. Very few.

'That night all man, all woman, all child for many mile around knew only to look down. Down at feet, down on to ground, down into earth away from sky. They stay in houses, curtains drawn. All doors locked. Stable bar. Animals tie away.

'No one look upwards because all knew who ride in sky when moon is full and wind is so wild; who ride that raging wind, more wild, the better for her: witch. Grey witch of wilderness, looking for companion to join her that night. Man, woman, child or beast – it not matter. For she only want their soul.

'How they know this was witch's night? They knew because all had seen sign. Witch's sign. Wee lamby –

poor beast. Wee lamby, strung up by heels from gate to forest; throat cut. And on sorry hide, written in poor creature's blood was score bold: 'Come to me. Aye. *Come to me.*'

'And when villagers see this awful thing, all ran at once for homes, to schools where they did carry children away in arms; to fields to find all working men who miss to hear news. And they lock doors and wait.

'But that night, as villagers cower and pray for morning, there came stranger to their midst. An upright man, wandering priest who said sermons wherever folk were to listen, he did know nothing of witch's word. It was first time in this part of country. Distant place far, far from cosmopolitan city and well travel roads, rarely trouble by visitor, he was draw by secrecy – promise of place so little to speak of, barely map. New place for him to spread Good Lord Word.

'As he approach dirty cobbles of narrow little main street, buffet and blow by wind, soak to skin by driving rain, he hurry on, cheery at thought of warm fire and bed for night. All he must do, he reason, was to find village inn and all would being well. Hour was not yet late.

'Behind him he hear storm gather apace, awful howling of wind rise like banshee scream over trees. Terrible shrieking – Devil's very own sound, he think as he did draw cloak about person.

'He stop at first house on street. Curtains were drawing but he detect movement within, so he knock and hope to ask for direction to inn. He wait but no one come. He knock again, horrible wind tearing at back, making flesh of neck crawl and creep. It was true ungodly sound – but still no one answer door.

'He move on to next house and knock harder. Once more he could see movement within – and her voices. Children. Light in hall, but no answer. No one did come to door.

'"Hello," he call out, rapping at door with cane. "Hello?" No answer. "I seek only direction," he say. "Road to inn, nearest inn, if you please." Still no answer.

'Shaking head, sadden by villager lack of charity, he turn about way he had come into village, thinking perhaps he miss sign which would be taking him to inn.

'That was when he saw her, sitting astride broom, hovering in air: witch. With lifeless eyes she gaze at him, pale face half-turning towards moon, mouth open so he glimpse awful yellow teeth.

'"Come to me," she whisper. "Come to me."

'He stumble back against door on which he did just knock.

'"Begone," he did call. "Begone, Devil creature!"

'She merely laugh and repeat cruel words: "Come to me." She advance towards him, raise spindle arm and wag claw which Devil give her for finger. "Come to me."

'"No!" he cry, sensing stench of foul breath – smell of disease and death. He did spin round and pound at villager door. "Please, for love of God, let me inside."

'"God will not help you now," crow witch. "God

cannot help you, for you are mine. Come to me, bonnie lad. Come to me."

'Priest ran to next house, and next. One after other he hammer at door of every property in street, but all to no avail. Inside villagers whimpered and covered ears.

' "Cowards!" he did cry to them. "Will not one man help me?"

' "No," whisper witch. "None will. Now," she hiss, "come to me."

' "Curse on all of you, every one," scream priest. "Curse on every one of you that you will never forget day, this day, what you have done. Curse you all."

'And witch nodded, for she knew what priest's curse meant. Abandoning God, he give himself over to her. To Devil. And she took him away.

'To this day priest curse haunts village – sad place, not so very far from here. When wind is in trees and moon is full, priest tormented soul will pass from one door to next, knocking, knocking. Knocking all night. It hammer at doors and rap at windows, tap on glass so none may rest within. Come stormy night and not one person in village ever sleeps.'

28 August
I do not remember falling into sleep – but I must have. Next morning I wake on armchair, empty bottle on table in front of me – fireplace cold. I check time and did see it was late, nearly nine. In daylight room look so different. Walls appear rough, of only stone. No curtain over

window although these I was sure to have seen previous night. No bowl on table – no apple. Table it look sorry and rot. Above fireplace was no picture and on mantel-piece no clock. What is this? I ask myself, staring at empty armchair in front of me. Did I imagine these thing?

I call out for Uncle Donald, but no answer. Thinking he might be sleep in bed I rise to feet and proceed through little doorway and climb stair. But I find nothing: no bed, only empty room – more stone wall and dirty window. Things appear so different in darkness, night before.

I go down stairs and find front door open, swing gently in wind.

'Hello, Uncle Donald?' I shout. 'Where are you?' I listen, expect to hear at least sound of dog clinking collar.

Then outside I hear sound of engine approaching and I remember: postman. So I hurry outside to see, to my surprise how close was house in fact to road. I see red postman van and wave. He slow. I wave again and he stop.

'Hello?' he say.

'Yes, hello,' I say.

He look at me with confusion.

'Moment,' I tell him and retreat once more inside cottage. 'Donald?' I cry out. 'Uncle Donald?'

I go back to edge of road where postman stand.

'My friend say you please give me lift to garage. My car it crash,' I say.

'Och aye.' He look more happy, as if now he know something. 'Mercedes. I see her on way up Glen first thing. Nasty knock, by look o' things.'

'Indeed,' I answer. 'Can you give me lift?'

'Och aye. Nae bother.'

I get into postal van, thinking I will return to thank Uncle Donald for hospitality once I have new car from hiring company. I look back and see cottage – decrepit place scarce fit for life I think. No doubt he is very poor, I muse and, as I am millionaire, I consider offering gift of money.

'Strange chap,' I say as we drive away. It is sunny day.

'Sorry, sir?'

'I say he is peculiar fellow.' I gesticulate with thumb towards old cottage.

Postman look confuse again. 'I dinna ken whit ye mean, sir.'

'I say that gentleman who is living here is eccentric, is he not?'

'Well, sir, I wouldna know.' He scratch head. 'No one live there for – well, not for many year.'

'No one?'

'I dinna think so. What did friend look like?'

I tell him and he grow pale.

'Did he, by chance, have dog?' he ask me.

'Oh yes,' I say.

'And did he wear sunglasses?'

'Yes.' I feel all it was not well.

'Well, sir. There was man who live here –

called Donald. He look awfa lot like man you talk about.'

'Yes, Donald, that was name.'

'Auld Uncle Donald . . . But it canna hae been him. No.' Postman shake head. 'Auld Uncle Donald is dead gone last twenty five years.'

I feel sickness in stomach.

'Aye, dog ran into forest during storm. Frighten by lightning, maybe. That night was one hell of wind. Awfa storm. People think Donald go out after dog – and this was last thing poor man did ever do.'

'What did happen him?' I ask.

'Well, some say he slip on wet leaves – others that he was hit by car speeding up hill in night – maybe the driver didna see him in the storm. People say many things. Many, many things. Either way, he hit head and roll into the ditch. And he drown, poor man. He drown.'

I say little more on journey but return to town where I arrange for new hire car and salvage of wreck one. I did not return to cottage – nor will I ever.

This is last time I will speak of Uncle Donald.

In afternoon

New car is beautiful model Saab. Is still beautiful summer day and imaginings of night before have been forgotten in sunshine.

All of Salmon will be transported in ice to Swiss Alps. I have guarantee of refrigeration.

(Editors' note: This page is dominated by a large line drawing of a fish, possibly a salmon, and a laughing fisherman.)

Heather

A note of heather. Nothing can compare with scent of heather. Like lemon honey – sweet but difficult. This is wild smell. Through August I have seen heather grow from pink to purple. In places heather has already become brown. Somewhere, heather it is burned, smoking blowing across hills like shroud of summer. Because summer is to go so soon. Gunshot at bird, and the colder rain. Fisherman standing on riverbank quite still. This is Scotland that I have found. A beautiful place I will come to once more. I would bring Anna here, Anna to end her days and mine too. We would live in lonely place, chase rabbit and fish for salmon.

30 August

My return to Swiss Alps. I am pleased to be back. Anna greet me like demon possessed by helicopter tail. No more will I think of Uncle Donald.

1 September

So Otto did visit Erwin and Ursula. Now they will be withdraw threatening litigation and have made decision to move towards south, New Zealand perhaps. This is so wise. I did not ask Otto to visit them, and I did in fact implore them not to seek judgement of court against him. Otto does not acknowledge such thing. So they move by their own hand and my conscience is clear.

No more thought of Uncle Donald.

5 September
I have now purchase former residence belonging to Erwin and Ursula. This is only property to hand for many miles and in my own hands will guarantee privacy and seclusion. What shall I do with this place?

1 Destroy
2 Rent to assistant (although assistant change)
3 Plan for Pig House

Detail of Pig House
I shall explain here nature of 'Pig House'. My experiences with Moses, pig of Inverness, have led me to conclude that pig is special beast. Man may descend from ape, but if pig had animal descend from it, would be similar to man, only better.

Moses did demonstrate:

Ability to count.

Ability to complete complicated task.

Wilful disobedience to do stupid animal task (i.e. sit, when standing is perfectly good).

And much else (to be detailed tomorrow, when time will permit me).

(Editors' note: There are no further entries.)

241

HOW TO MAKE POLISH CHRISTMAS

2.12.1989

Dear Uncle Kasimir,

How are you and Anna Karenina, your dog? You don't know me but you know my big brother Urban who is doing acting at university. So hello!

I was wondering if you could help me with something else because I am in the folk group at our church in Faversham, where we live, and this year I have been voted on the committee to do with raising money for Xmas. It all gets given to starving children, so it's really a good cause. Every year the committee does a different kind of Xmas for old pensioners in the parish. Last year it was a Scottish and we sprayed everything with fake snow and made everyone wear tartan hats. I said we should do a Polish Xmas this year and Mum said to ask you since when you were little you used to have proper Polish Xmas every year!

If there are any tips or advice you can suggest I'd be really grateful. If you're too busy don't worry, but it would be really nice to do it!

Lots of love,
Tommy Winicki

9 December 1989

My dearest Tommy,

What is Xmas? Please say only Christmas.

How good it is to hear from you. I am in good health and so is Anna. I am delighted to hear that you are thinking of old people at Christmas. As an old person I often feel neglected, especially by those close to me (who are not) – although your mother did send a letter in the summer.

I am also in excellent spirits now I hear that you are going to church at Faversham. Many years ago, as you must know, I helped your mother and father to move to this area on condition of them lighting a candle to St Jude for me every day in the shrine. I doubt very much that they still do this, with 'modern' life and washing machines. However, it would make me very happy if you might find time to light a candle for me, as the intervention by St Jude is always much needed, despite my good health.

Of course I will be only too happy to tell you about Polish Christmases of my youth, which I can recall like only yesterday. I believe that very little has changed and that, today, Christmas is still celebrated much as I shall describe. What a pity that I shall be celebrating Christmas on my own this year, with only Anna. This place can seem so very lonely towards the end of a year. Perhaps you might speak to your mother about simplicity of travelling to Swiss Alps at Christmas.

When I was a young boy in Kraków it was custom to celebrate Christmas on 6 December: St Nicholas Day.

However, unlike other youths of my neighbourhood I was lucky enough to enjoy Christmas again on 24 December and then once more on 25 December. I have three Christmases.

Let me explain. On 6 December we have traditional celebration at home in Kraków. This was often sombre affair involving traditional carol and prayer. Then about 20 December entire family would travel from Kraków to Free City of Gdańsk, then by cruiser across Baltic to Helsinki in Finland and finally in jolly carriage to city of Turku on eve of 23 December, where we would have Christmas again with family friend Mikki.

The time I shall describe it was typical of early 1920s, the happy times before the war. There were five of us: myself, of course, my sisters Wanda and Lotta, and my brothers Alec and Kristof. Wanda would have been ten or eleven. I was perhaps seven, and so Alec would be the eldest of us there aged twelve (although Albert was in fact eldest but already at military camp); Lotta was very young and noisy, no more than four or five, still crawl, and Kristof would be maybe one year older. Also with us was Captain Lasiewicz, who we call Lasi, once great leader of military regiment but now cuckoo in the head after brain injury – and he work as gardener at our house in Kraków. At this time I did not yet have dog. Estimable tutor Kuss was also absent from family Christmas, preferring to spend festive season on his own in library.

Family friend Mikki was distinguished naval admiral to whom my father owed life after diplomatic incident in Finnish civil war, 1918. My father loved Mikki as if he was brother – perhaps more. Certainly more than Uncle Felix, later to die by his own hand. I love Mikki too, with long white beard and smell of tobacco and whisky. Always he have great pipe hanging from mouth trailing smoke as he moved from room to room like steam boat – lurching as if from waves due to wooden leg.

At once when we arrived father and Mikki would embrace, weep and drink wodka by fire in great study – although smaller than our own. Study it was warmest room in this great mansion set high on hill, so we children were at first allowed to stand quietly by hearth while servants carried cases in from coach, wiped snow from our shoes and so on.

'Ha, Mikki!' my father bellow as if to join battle.

'Stanisław! Stanisław! Old ox!' Mikki cry. 'Ahaka!' He did cough like this every time.

Glasses would be thrown inside sizzling fireplace, torching flames to rise like wild petrochemical ignition as fire lick at remaining spirit. They then pour more Wodka while mother went about house checking to make safe bottles, harpoon and so on, accoutrements of seafarer, for children. As she did this both men would punch each other stomachs.

'Ha, Mikki, you old buffalo, what girth!' shouted my father before collapsing from Mikki punch hard in gut.

'Ha! Ha! Stanisław, ahaka, the great military general is old woman bearing child, ho ho! Ahaka.' At this my father he would gather himself from floor and punch back at Mikki, who this time would fall and drop pipe on to carpet, and teeth (teeth were false). Both men proceed to punch and swear while children watched in wonder. Eventually mother would run into room and usher us to pantry, closing door to study with sigh.

Pantry was smaller room but still perhaps warmer and in here whole family – although not of course my father – would feed by old servant woman, widow called Oili, who had hump and grey hair piled on head like snake-jug. She did sing Finnish songs and ladle thick broth into bowls and Lasi accompany her on sailor squeeze-box. Lasi was good man who came with us wherever we were going.

After meal we children would run about house playing games in rare expression of joyous mirth while mother blow eggs, including large ones (perhaps ostrich. 'Cat' I say once, as infant. 'No, Kasimir,' said my mother in family joke, 'cat does not have egg'). Outside it was the darkness and snow; inside lamps glowed in long corridors with locked rooms, webs and creaking boards separate by deep plunging crack. How we did play, screaming with fear at monstrous apparition perhaps trapped in chamber and bats we imagined swooping from ceiling. Lasi join us, leaping from shadows as in trepidation we approached and scream-ing, swinging chain around head and throwing dead leaves from pockets. Mikki was living by himself at this time, his wife having departed, and so other than several servants this entire enormous house was like winter palace.

One room after another we explore, my sister Wanda playing fool and rolling across carpets like clown or dropped coin. In some rooms there were stuffed animal like bear, elk, and wolf, who all have beady eye for naughty children and did scare us to scream and run into next room where we might find model boats in glass casing, or spoils of many years sailing high seas: spear of native from Java, drums, dodo head (this fake, I am sure), shrinking human head and coconut palm. Cannon.

It was tradition we play like this until we hear gun shot from down stairs. At this sound we scurry from wherever we did find ourselves back to study. Servant would open door with creak on hinge, and inside all was dark but for single candle on little low table now placed in front of fire. To each side of this table was one armchair: on left was sitting my father and on the right sit Mikki, shotgun lying across knees after shot, plaster fallen from ceiling to floor all around him like snow. He did dust shoulders and head, light pipe and laugh softly.

'A drink for my friend! Ahaka!' he bellow at servant, as if calling to sailor in typhoon wind. Servant hurry to produce one more bottle of wodka, even though father was by this time often sunk deep in chair and snoring.

'Now then, children,' Mikki begin as servant close door behind us. When latch fell in place always it make one final sound, click like hand on clock at end of time. 'I am delighted to have you here with me this Christmas Eve. Ahaka. Please, sit down.' All of us sat rapidly in line facing him, like ducks on pond and he the hunter. 'Young master Kasimir, ahaka,' he would say, raising hand and pointing bent old finger at me. 'What is it our tradition to do every night before Christmas Eve?'

In fire log crackle, shadows dancing. Outside wild gale it blow like demon, punctuate only by sound of servant chopping wood.

'To tell ghost story,' I reply.

'Ahaka. Very good,' he say, stroking pipe, his finger tremble. 'Very, very good.'

And Mikki tell us such terrifying tale that my heart afterwards beat like blacksmith hammer on sword blade and teeth chatter like machine-gun fire. Wanda cry once so my father did wake and sit forward, scowl on face – a thing more terrifying than ghost story itself, and which brought us to complete silence. A silence that last long after my father snore again, and Mikki with him.

This happen as soon as story was complete. We used to sit in complete silence, so still, too frightened to move or almost to breathe. If I could not have breathed I would happily have die. Eventually door to study open and my mother did whisper to us: 'Are there any good children in here who deserve Christmas treat?'

Silently we did arise without waking men, so careful because not only treat but lives depended on it, and tiptoe from room as quickly as any child can do. As I left this room I always glance at ceiling to see holes of many Christmas past, where gunshot had signalled ghost story and after which we children flee from this place – and I think that anything it could happen.

But outside room, in gay light of hall lamps all was at once completely different and so merry. Lasi gambol from pantry, skipping with high steps like Cossack (but in stocking only, in case of noise) and carrying tray of bonbon. Silently, like magic sprite with curious expression he would lead us to grand living room where mother was waiting with eggs, many sheet of paper, paints and cutting knife so we could make traditional decoration. Lasi place tray on floor to be fell upon like little sparrows in field of corn, until all were gone.

First we make paper cuttings, traditional Polish custom called Wycinanki of which I have enclosed one example (hastily cut – it is Christmas tree). At this time mother would also remind us of previous celebrations on 6 December, St Nicholas's day. On that day we had received either gingerbread biscuits (pierniki) if we had been good, or twigs if we had been bad. I receive twigs however I did behave because it was good to build character and allay sloth. Then, too, I make cutting of Christmas tree, as it is a simple shape. Little Lotta, even when so young, make beautiful cutting of nativity. If war did not end dreams in blindness perhaps she would be great artist, like you cousin Gabi will surely be. And then we go to bed, to dream of the next day – of Christmas Eve.

Christmas Eve was of far greater importance than Christmas day and on eve of Christmas Eve I would keep awake long into night-time listening to howl of wind, and distant uproar from library when my father and Mikki awake periodically to drink Wodka and jest. In spite of men voice I imagine infant Jesus lying tender in mange overlook by sheeps and cattle, shining glittery star high above in the air, and long for excitement of next day to be delivered all at once, like explosion.

I feel hungry, too, and imagine how great hunger would become the next day. It was custom to fast whole of Christmas Eve until special meal in evening time: Wigilia. Before this we would clean house and arrange Christmas tree cut from forest at dawn by my father and Mikki (for they did not retire to bed at all when they were meeting like this – only they sleep in chairs when stupor came upon them). Already as I thought this I could hear noise of servant sharpening two-head axe they would take with them at first light for task.

One time Mikki did chop his foot from his leg – but fortunately it was wooden leg. I was ordered to find missing foot in forest before Wigilia feast and I set out into snowy wastes with long stick to check for drift and shotgun in case of wolf or boar, praying that no more snow would fall and that I would be able to follow father and Mikki footsteps to forest – what route they take, in curves. This I did, and I found stump of tree they bring back to the house – but no foot, only cinders from tinker fire. It did seem that some others had follow my father and Mikki into forest and chanced upon foot, using it as fuel. For once it was not I who was to pay. Mikki let loose slavering hounds in forest for tinker.

So to Christmas Eve. Through day we set tree and mistletoe for evil spirits (over front door). Oili and mother place wheat in dining room – in corners of room and beneath tablecloth to avert misery. Women then set table with one extra place in case of extra visitor (or the dead, such as Grandfather Regus or Great-grandfather Marek). Normally Polish go to great lengths to invite guest for dinner to take this place, but at Mikki house we always knew who would come: Englishman called Cecil from gatehouse.

My father love Cecil almost as greatly as Mikki, this strange and dignify Englishman with sparkle wit who could not return to England (I know not why). He so often say 'Pardon me' or 'Pon my word', to which we children make mimickry all Christmas day. He was very thin man with eyeglass and handkerchief in pocket, tweedy suit and walking cane.

All this time children watch sky and run shouting to mother at sign of first star – for this was signal at last to eat. This commotion it wake Mikki and father and they join us at table to say prayer and enjoy Oplatek, special holy bread wafer which all share. Servant would fetch Cecil from gatehouse to join with us and he arrive with arm of presents.

Meal was of food from forest, field, lakes, and orchard – no meat. This was good day to be animal! Sometimes meal last for eternity including maybe thirteen course: mushroom soup, barszcz (beetroot soup) with uszka (small dumpling) or almond soup. Pierogi (small pastry parcel) next with different filling, and potato – and noodle with poppy seed. Children in particular did not like next course of fish (but we eat all the same): jelly carp – all different kind of river fish prepare in different way, but usual carp. For dessert all kind of fruit and ginger biscuit, and Krupnik to drink (famous drink).

This was all very boring for children who wanted only present. However we would be very good throughout for terror of punishment by father. Not once we suffer such punishment but of all bad things to do in one year we would believe that bad at this time would be dealt with most severely. So we were good.

After dinner father leave Mikki and Cecil and go to barns to feed creatures with leftovers or similar. It is Polish traditional belief that on Christmas Eve animals do speak. Children follow with mother in awe silence and approach old donkey Neddy, in stall.

'Hello, children, ahaka,' said donkey. 'Do you have something tasty for me? Ahaka.'

One child solemnly approach talking beast with treat and feed into mouth. Neddy sometimes spit food back on to floor at which father darken in face and place hand on holster (always he wear gun). My mother did dive to his side and weep: 'No, Stanisław, not now, not Christmas Eve, think of children and Holy Spirit, please! Infant Jesus!' and so on.

'Ahaka,' say donkey and he laugh.

Father would relent and we pass to piglets in pen. Another child did approach piglets with morsel.

'Hello, little child, ahaka,' say one piglet. 'Yum yum, how lovely.'

'Pon my word,' say one other piglet. 'Bravo, young man, jolly good show.'

Never once did any of us children request to know why all animals would make cough like Mikki or utter preposterous English phrase. Only after Mikki have surgery and make whistle when he breath I did come to suspect truth. Perhaps it was coincidence for talking ass to make whistling, but not also piglet and hen.

Following animal feast it was time for presents to be exchange, what fun. Mikki and father have stiff drink again, in prepare for family sleigh ride, while remaining family congratulate one another on splendid present. For my brothers and sisters I always buy book from small shop near house in Kraków, usually of fairy tale such as Hans Christian Andersen or perhaps biblical tales. For my mother I always give one silken white rose, which she wear on Christmas day.

My mother and father did provide for us wonderful presents, although many I was forbidden to use until attaining majority (such as revolver). One time my father give to me beautiful-looking little book he find on visit to Germany, called *Der Struwwelpeter*. After reading this book I was very sick with fear at having fingers snip off, because I did suck thumb!

Finally we have short traditional sleigh ride. This was terrify but brisk and stimulating experience on Mikki sledge in dead of night, with whip crack and horses thunder through Turku cobble streets. My father, Mikki and Cecil take reigns together while my mother huddle with children at back of sledge, all of us singing Kolêdy, traditional Polish Carol which are very important part of Polish Christmas. Several time we did have minor accident and have to stop for extreme apologies and so on.

All adults then go to midnight Mass while children retire to bed with lovely kiss.

I hope, my young man, that this will tell you everything you must know about Polish Christmas. Of all Christmas celebration it is without doubt the most magnificent.

Please pass to your mother my love and best wishes. Since last year I have extensive renovations made to my house, making it ideal for winter break. Perhaps you will mention this. I have also sent package for yourself and rest of family. Please give my love to your brother and tell him that I would wish he should break leg. With much love and affection.

Kindest regards,
Uncle Kasimir

14 December 1989

Dear Uncle Kasimir,

Thanks a lot for all of your advice about Polish Christmas. It was all very helpful and we will be having a Polish Christmas party at the church hall on Christmas Eve before midnight Mass just like in reality. But I don't know if you'll get this in time or not, because I really need to know something else, very soon or we won't be able to do it. Father Hamish says he doesn't know what Krupnik is, and I don't either. I asked Mrs Robinson at school but she never knows what things are made from, even though she teaches cookery as well as biology. Mum knows what it is but says she doesn't know what all the ingredients are.

Can you tell me what Krupnik is made of, please? Also, I wondered what the third Christmas day was, because you only say what happened on two of them in your letter, although at the beginning you said that there were three but that last thing is just if you have time because I don't want to bother you too much.

I can't wait to open my present! Thanks a lot! Urban is back for the Christmas holidays now and he laughed a lot when I told him you wanted to break his legs, which I thought was really funny.

Lots of love, and to AK III,
Tommy
PS: Mum has sent you a really big parcel – we hope you like it. She says we must come and stay with you in the summer.

Telegram, 18 December 1989
Dear Tommy STOP I am sending this to you by telegram to enable Polish Christmas celebration STOP Here is recipe for Krupnik STOP 2 cup vodka (or more to taste) STOP 1 cup honey STOP 1 cup water STOP 6 cloves STOP 1 cinnamon stick STOP a vanilla bean STOP

jotting of fresh grate nutmeg STOP piece of lemon peel to length of thumb, just zest (yellow) STOP 1 inch piece of orange peel, merely zest (orange) STOP And Christmas number three was spend with Cecil who have old jalopy and we go ride in winter forest STOP No more sleigh ride on Christmas day on account of my mother and nerves. STOP Wesolych Swiat Bozego Narodzenia

THE LAST LETTER

14 June 1999

My dear Gabi,

Naturally I would usually ask how you are, but of course I know this already. Your mother telephone me last night with news of your circumstances – first time she has contacted me in many months, so I realise from the outset it was a serious matter.

Please do not feel that I wish to meddle in your affairs, but as one who has also lost love and grieved as you must grieve now, I have felt compunction to write to you expressing my profound sorrow. Also, it is my belief that since your mother did remarry to Bavarian, that fruit of this union Oscar is apple of their eye. Did I receive letter to tell me of Gabi's 18th birthday? No, I did not. But of course I make note of date, as Kasimir does with every date, and sent gift of money to aid studies in art (and you very kindly thank me in letter). And do I receive postcards every year from advertising 'executive' Oscar, telling me of his adventures? No, I do not. But on wall above my desk I can now look up and see postcard from Turin, Malta, Tasmania in Australia where you take river trip, New York and islands of Orkney. I would not know that Oscar is 'executive' if Gabi did not tell me. You may tell him he has great distance to travel, not for holiday but to be man. This much he will understand.

But all this is to move from the point. My poor Gabi, you should feel most welcome to come visit me in Swiss Alps at any time. I mention this to faithful hound Anna Karenina III and her ears stand to attention like Soviet guard at tomb of Lenin. She say, 'Poor Gabi, abandon by stupid husband she must come to Swiss Alps and together we will walk after mountain goats. Gabi is lovely girl, honour daughter of Kasimir, always bright flower, who deserve much better than Dutchman "Chris".'

Anna Karenina III is exceptional judge of character. She tell me she would seek out this Chris with mistress to bite both, if only dog could travel freely. I too would inflict punishment on him worthy of my own father, great military general – or perhaps of estimable tutor Kuss if I could travel freely. But I am now old man, sad of heart, in dismay at sadness of his niece Gabi and in place just of his making. Old man writing at his desk when he should be with you, to embrace you in sorrow.

From time to time I do ask myself, what would my own father do at this? Would he kill or only maim? Would he set off at dawn with trusted crossbow and small pack of dog? Would he simply look at Dutchman and make tear come to eyes? In world of my father, in time of his, he could do one and everything. But in world of mine – our world – what could he do? As much, now, as any man. As much and as little as nothing. I know this is true. This is no world for great man or woman. To be great in this world is to be of one moment only, because this greatness it is to be bestow and at once remove in winking of eye. So, perhaps, is it now better we are all ordinary? Still, I believe my Gabi is special, and perhaps this is why she now has this pain. Ordinary husband has run away with ordinary woman – run, run, like all little creature from great thing. I am glad you have artist friend Peter to comfort you. Perhaps with new exhibition you will both be great.

You have tell me before that Chris is pleasing Bavarian. I remember this. In love one must please only self. I learn this a long time ago to great cost.

If there is anything I can do for you please tell me. Should money help I can give you as much as you require. If you would like to visit me, I will pay for journey. Whatever you should want, I wish only that it will make you happy.

You are indeed my special girl.

With love at this time,
Your Uncle Kasimir

AFTERWORD

Of course I responded to Kasimir's letter, but I received no reply. This was completely out of character for him. In the past we'd enjoyed such a happy correspondence and shared such wonderful memories. Instead, just as I was on the point of telephoning him, about a month after I wrote to him, his old camphor-wood chest arrived by courier with no return address. Discovering its contents I wasted no time calling him; but the number was dead. I got in touch with William, who used a journalistic contact in Switzerland to find out that it had been sent from the main post office in the nearest town to Kasimir's villa; but there was no record of who had posted it.

We travelled to Switzerland and found the villa deserted – locked up and in a bad state of repair. The whole place was so run down it was impossible to tell how long it had been uninhabited. A chewed dog toy, a rubber bone with a bell in it, sat at the foot of the steps leading to the entrance; that was the only sign of life.

We tried to speak to the neighbours (few though they were), but they avoided us. Eventually we persuaded the police to check out the property – which they insisted on doing without us – but they found nothing odd. The place was tidy, they said. Everything was in order. No crime had taken place.

Several years have now passed since Uncle Kasimir's disappearance. Sadly, in all that time we have heard nothing from him. Although it's easy to conclude that this means he is no longer with us, both of us prefer to hope that is not the case.

We miss him dearly and sincerely hope that if he is alive, and he picks up a copy of this book, he'll finally get back in touch.

GC

CZERNIAK FAMILY TREE

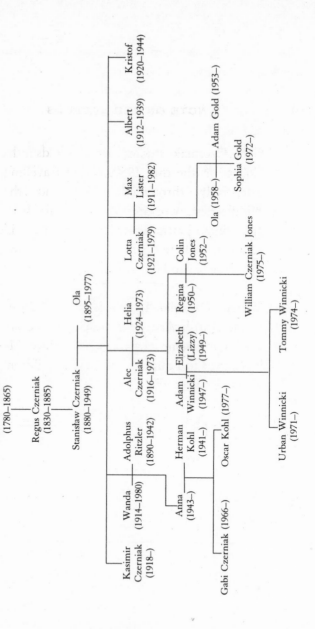

A NOTE ON THE AUTHORS

Gabi Czerniak studied art at Goldsmiths College in the mid 1980s before travelling extensively throughout Asia and the Middle-East, working as a portrait artist and photo-journalist. She now lives in London, where she lectures part-time in Cultural Studies.

William Czerniak-Jones served as an officer in the British Army for eight years before leaving to pursue a career in journalism. He is married to Laura and has three children: Holly, Frances and Craig.